Turquois and Spanish Mines in New Mexico

Frontispiece. Turquois Mine, Cerrillos, New Mexico, c. 1881-82. Collections in the Museum of New Mexico. Photo by George C. Bennett.

Turquois and Spanish Mines in New Mexico

Stuart A. Northrop

UNIVERSITY OF NEW MEXICO PRESS
Albuquerque

Turquois and Spanish Mines in New Mexico is excerpted from the book *Minerals of New Mexico,* by Stuart A. Northrop, copyright 1944, 1959 by the University of New Mexico Press.

Manufactured in the United States of America
Library of Congress Catalog Card Number 75-7474

International Standard Book Number 0-8263-0371-4

Contents

List of Illustrations

PART I

The History of New Mexico Mineralogy and Mining

PREHISTORIC UTILIZATION OF MINERALS

The historic period of New Mexico began about 1540, but the prehistoric inhabitants of the State made extensive use of a variety of minerals and rocks many centuries before that date.[1]

Sandia Man, of perhaps more than 20,000 years ago, and Folsom Man, of about 10,000 years ago, did not, apparently, make use of very many minerals, except for several forms of quartz, such as agate, chalcedony, and chert. Sandia Cave, near Placitas, is in Sandoval County, at the north end of the Sandia Mountains. According to Hibben (1941), this cave contains three cultural layers, from the top down: 1) recent, 2) Folsom, and 3) Sandia. Artifacts in the Sandia layer are composed mostly of chert, although fragments of chalcedony occur; much of the material may have had a local source. Artifacts in the Folsom layer include chips, flakes, and scrapers made of Pedernal chalcedony,[2] and Folsom points "of materials approaching the chalcedony classification but apparently of a different source." These Folsom points are composed of white chalcedony, "brownish agate chalcedony," and mottled purplish chert. Bryan (1941, p. 58) concluded that the Sandia culture is a little older than 25,000± years and the Folsom culture a little younger than 25,000± years. However, Antevs (1941, p. 41) stated that, although Bryan and Ray "are inclined to give the Folsom Culture at Lindenmeier [Colorado] an age of 25,000 years," he would date the Lindenmeier Folsom at "little more than 10,000 years." Carbon-14 measurements of fragments of mammoth tusk from the Sandia layer of Sandia Cave suggest an age of 25,000–30,000 years,[3] according to Crane (1955), who adds:

> "The great age of the Sandia tusk naturally raises the question whether it is contemporary with the evidences of habitation among which it was found, or whether, instead, we have discovered that among the men who inhabited the cave there were archeologists who collected and brought home tusks belonging to earlier times."

Artifacts in the recent, topmost layer of Sandia Cave are "all of the multihued and usually translucent chalcedony of the Pedernal variety. . . ."

---

1. The writer has had the opportunity over a period of years of assisting in, and checking, the identification of abundant archeologic material of a geologic nature, especially from sites in the Jemez and Chaco regions.

2. For a description of Pedernal chalcedony and chert and prehistoric pits and quarries, see Bryan (1938; 1939) and Church and Hack (1939).

3. According to George Agogino of Eastern New Mexico University, ". . . I feel that the age of the Sandia level is roughly that of Clovis, that is roughly 11,500 years old. This is based on geologic evidence plus typological characteristics of the artifacts themselves. The earlier age of more than 25,000 was based on the belief that the Pleistocene period ended roughly 25,000 years ago rather than the currently accepted age of 10,000 years ago" (personal communication, October 1974).

Howard (1935, p. 105–123) has reviewed geological and archeological work in New Mexico, especially of the Clovis-Portales area. In discussing Folsom artifacts, he notes that a point or projectile point may be a spear-point, atlatl-dart point, or arrow point. Folsom points were presumably used with spear-throwers. In general, Folsom points from many localities were made of jasper, chert, or chalcedony. Howard (1935, p. 108–109) states:

> "In connection with the kind of material used in producing artifacts, there seems to be considerable confusion. Most of it, it is readily agreed, is a cryptocrystalline variety of quartz, but as to whether it should be called chert or flint, jasper or chalcedony, is very difficult to decide, since the differences are largely microscopical. Color appears to be the main guide megascopically, Tarr differentiating chert from flint on the basis that chert is usually white and other lighter colors, and flint black or dark gray."

Antevs (1935) dated the Folsom artifacts from Clovis at 12,000–13,000 years old. In this connection it may be noted that Libby (1952, p. 82–85) gave the following radiocarbon dates for New Mexico:

	Years
Folsom site	4,283 ± 250
Cochise charcoal on the Wet Leggett	4,508 ± 680
Bat Cave	5,931 ± 310

Later, Libby (1954, p. 138–139) gave a radiocarbon date of 7,432 ± 300 years for charcoal from Burnet Cave, Guadalupe Mountains.

In describing the Cochise and Mogollon sites of Pine Lawn Valley, southwest of Reserve, Catron County, Martin, Rinaldo, and Antevs (1949) noted that Cochise artifacts of 3,500 to 5,000 years ago include such items as:

Ground and Pecked Stone

- Handstones
  - Manos
  - Rubbing stones
  - Pestles
- Milling stones
  - Metates
  - Mortars
- Worked slabs
- Polishing stones
- Hammerstones
- Stone dishes
- Abrading stones
- Pipes

Chipped Stone

- Projectile points
- Knives
- Scrapers
- Choppers
- Drills
- Hoes

No attempt will be made here even to review the imposing array of evidence for the prehistoric use of minerals in New Mexico but inasmuch as a comprehensive résumé of the Chaco Canyon material is available, the evidence for this region will be summarized. According to Brand, Hawley, Hibben, and others (1937, p. 55–62), the following minerals, all of which were utilized during the period A.D. 750–1150, have been recovered from excavations in Chaco Canyon, San Juan County:

- Aragonite
- Azurite
- Calcite (crystals)
  - Calcareous tufa
  - Chalk
  - Limestone
- Copper
- Galena (crystals)
- Garnet (probably pyrope)
- Gilsonite
- Goethite
- Gypsum (rock)
  - Alabaster
  - Selenite
- Hematite
  - Red ocher
  - Reddle
- Jet
- Kaolinite
- Limonite
  - Yellow ocher
- Malachite
- Muscovite
- Pyrite
- Quartz
  - Rock crystal
  - Milky quartz
  - Agate
  - Chalcedony
  - Chert
  - Flint
  - Jasper
  - Onyx
  - Petrified wood
- Serpentine
  - Picrolite
- Sulfur
- Talc
  - Steatite or
    - Soapstone
- Turquois

This is a total of 40 minerals, including 21 species and 19 additional varieties. Many of these are native to the Chaco region, but the following were probably imported: azurite, copper, galena, garnet, malachite, muscovite, serpentine, talc, and turquois. Of turquois, Brand remarks:

> "This semi-precious stone was and is the most prized ornament material among the Indians of New Mexico. It was the material most commonly used for beads, pendants, inlays, etc., in the Chaco ruins, as at Pueblo Bonito where more than 50,000 pieces and items of turquoise were recovered by the Hyde Expedition."

For a discussion of prehistoric mining and working of turquois, see sections headed Prehistoric Mining and Archeology under Turquois in Part II of this book.

Some of the minerals recovered from the excavations were unworked; many, however, were worked. Some were used in making beads and pendants, and some as inlays in various ornamental objects; some were ground for pigments; some were used in making scrapers, knives, projectile points, polishing stones, hammerstones, etc.

In describing items found in several caves between Reserve and

Mogollon, ranging in age from A. D. 1100 to A. D. 1300, Martin, Rinaldo, and Bluhm (1954) note that artifacts were made of chalcedony, jasper, flint, and chert. They record beads made of turquois and jasper; pendants of malachite, gypsum, and calcite; and pigments of azurite, hematite, and malachite. Perhaps most intriguing were a number of quartz crystals, possibly used as drills, up to 5.6 cm long, 3.3 cm wide, and 2.5 cm thick.

S. H. Ball (1941) described the gems and ornamental stones used by American Indians before they came in contact with the white man. Although he includes numerous references to New Mexico, many of his citations refer simply to the Pueblo Indians of the Southwest and these, of course, may include records from Arizona and possibly certain other states. Minerals cited by Ball (1941, table 1) for the whole Southwest, but not by Brand and others (1937) for the Chaco area, include the following:

Actinolite
Apatite
Diopside
Feldspar
Fluorite
Magnesite
Magnetite
Olivine
Opal
Quartz
    Amethyst
    Carnelian
    Prase
    Smoky quartz
Scapolite
Sillimanite
Smithsonite (?)

As noted, some of these may not have been found in New Mexico ruins.

One of the most spectacular discoveries made by the prehistoric Indians of New Mexico was that of the triboluminescence of quartz. Kidder (1932, p. 93–94) has described and illustrated a "lightning set" found in the Pecos ruins. This set consists of a rectangular base with a groove in it and a bolster-shaped upper piece—both made of pure white vein quartz. Rapid friction by rubbing produces a strong glow in the dark. As Ball (1941, p. 31) remarks, "here we have a perfected machine perhaps 700 years old; the first Indian to observe the luminescence of quartz must have done so centuries earlier." Similar "lightning sets" or "glow-stones" have been found at several other localities in north-central New Mexico.

Finally, it may be noted that George Switzer identified a number of minerals among ceremonial articles found in pouches of Navajo singers by Kluckhohn and Wyman (1940). The area covered includes eastern Arizona as well as western New Mexico. Minerals are as follows:

Aragonite ("mirage stone")
Azurite
Clay (white)
Galena
Halite
Hematite
    Red ocher
    Specularite

Jet
Lignite
Limonite
  Yellow ocher
Malachite
Mendozite
Quartz
  Rock crystal
  Flint
Serpentine (Chrysotile)
Sulfur
Turquois

Mendozite and sulfur are used as fumigants. Kluckhohn and Wyman (1940, p. 47) commented that the "mirage stone" was

> "Made from gray and white striped (male) or white (female) aragonite, found only (as far as we know) on a mesa a few miles west of Los Lunas, New Mexico, and somewhere in the vicinity of Flagstaff, Arizona. Its source is guarded with much secrecy."

NEW MEXICO UNDER SPAIN

1535.—The first Europeans in New Mexico, possibly, were Alvar Núñez Cabeza de Vaca and three companions, one of whom was Esteban (a Negro or an Arab from Morocco). Some investigators hold that this party never entered New Mexico; others believe it did. At any rate, these men were given a copper rattle, and later some "silver" (mica?), and "antimony" (manganese ore or galena?) by certain Indians, possibly somewhere in southern New Mexico. The Indians told them of a large deposit of native copper, possibly the one at Santa Rita. Later, while in Mexico, they saw turquois, which the Indians said came from the north (Hallenbeck, 1940).

1539.—Fray Marcos de Niza, Esteban, and expedition started out from Mexico for Cibola (Zuni, New Mexico). Esteban was sent on ahead to explore and reached Cibola, where he was killed. Fray Marcos met many Indians in northern Mexico who possessed an abundance of turquois jewelry; he heard on several occasions that the portals and doorways at Cibola were decorated with turquois.

Capt. Melchior Díaz was sent out by Viceroy don Antonio de Mendoza to confirm the report of Fray Marcos. Díaz did not enter New Mexico, but he gathered hearsay evidence to the effect that the Indians at Cibola had an abundance of turquois and also that they obtained salt from a lake not far distant (Hammond and Rey, 1940).

1540.—Captain-General Francisco Vázquez de Coronado and his large force reached Cibola on July 7, and the conquest of New Mexico began. At Zuni, Coronado found turquois, some garnets, and "two points of emerald."[4] He noted "very good salt in crystals," from the Zuni or Que-

4. It is interesting to note that Whipple (1856, pt. 3, p. 109) translated this passage as "two pints of emeralds"! It would be of interest to learn what type of error this was—whether one of transcription, a *lapsus calami,* or a typographical one. At any rate, it may be assumed that the "emeralds" were peridots and that both peridots and garnets came from the vicinity of Fort Defiance, along the New Mexico–Arizona line.

mado salt lake, and also gold and silver. Castañeda, in his narrative of the expedition, mentions an abundance of turquois near Pecos; this turquois almost certainly came from Cerrillos.

1541.—Captain Barrionuevo was sent out to gather supplies. At Yuque-Yunque, near the junction of the Chama and Rio Grande, he found beautiful glazed pottery and

> "many ollas filled with a select shiny metal with which the Indians glazed their pottery. This was an indication that silver mines would be found in that land if they were sought" (Hammond and Rey, 1940).

Paul Reiter (1938, p. 24) noted that Bandelier thought this shiny metal may have been mica, but that Castañeda had referred to "earthenware glazed with antimony," and that recently Miss A. O. Shepard had suggested that galena may have been used as a glazing material. Reiter adds: "In considering the many later references to silver and shining metal, one wonders how often galena was confused."

Coronado and his expedition returned to Mexico in 1542.

1581.—Fray Agustín Rodríguez and Captain Francisco Sánchez Chamuscado led a small force into New Mexico. In September they were near Cerrillos and found mineral deposits in this region. They also visited the Estancia salt lakes and reported that these were "the best salines ever discovered by Christians."

1582.—On their way down the Rio Grande Valley, somewhere between the Sierra Ladrones and the San Mateo Mountains, they found "very good veins, rich in contents." The chronicler added: "There are so many deposits that it is indeed marvelous." Some of the samples "assayed at twenty *marcos* per hundred weight of ore" (Hammond and Rey, 1927).

1583.—Don Antonio de Espejo and Fray Bernardino Beltrán led an expedition into New Mexico. They reported finding mineral deposits, including "much antimony" (probably galena), along the Rio Grande Valley, possibly in the Organ, Caballo, and Manzano Mountains. Assays were made of ores from the Cerrillos-Ortiz Mountains region. At Zia, Indians gave them ore, presumably of copper, from the Jemez region (Bolton, 1916; Hammond and Rey, 1929).

1590–91.—An unauthorized and unlicensed attempt to colonize New Mexico was made by Capt. Gaspar Castaño de Sosa. Ore deposits were explored and assays made in the Cerrillos region (Bancroft, 1888).

1598.—The next attempt to colonize New Mexico was made by Don Juan de Oñate, leading a group of about 400 people. In July he established his headquarters and first Spanish settlement, San Juan,[5] at the pueblo of Oke, near the junction of the Chama and Rio Grande. Thence

5. The exact location is shown as being just northwest of the present San Juan Pueblo on the U. S. Geol. Survey topographic map of the San Juan Pueblo quadrangle.

he conducted a series of explorations (Bandelier, 1892; Bolton, 1916; Hammond, 1927). In August he visited the Jemez Hot Springs and noted deposits of sulfur and "alum" (possibly calcareous tufa). In October he visited the Estancia salt lakes. In November he went to Zuni and while there sent Capt. Marcos Farfán and four companions to explore the Zuni or Quemado salt lake. Upon their return to Zuni, lengthy testimony was taken. This seems to be the first detailed description of a New Mexico mineral deposit. Farfán reported that the salt bed "consists of solid salt as white and coagulated and as good as that of the sea, and even better." In the middle of the lake the salt "is so thick that it must be as deep as a long lance." And finally, "this witness believes it it true that in all Christianity, or outside it, there is nothing so magnificent, nor does our King have anything like it."[6]

Farfán's exploration of this salt lake was mentioned by Capt. Gaspar Pérez de Villagrá, one of Oñate's officers, in his *Historia de la Nueva México*, published in 1610. This epic poem is said to be not only the first poem written about any section of the United States, but also the first published history of an American commonwealth. In "Canto Diez y ocho" we find:

Y luego al Capitan Farfán mandaron,
Que fuesse à descubrir ciertas salinas,
De que grande noticia se tenia,
Y poniendo por obra aquel mandato,
Con presta diligencia, y buen cuidado,
En brebe dio la buelta, y dixo dellas,
Que eran tan caudalosas y tan grandes,
Que por espacio de una legua larga,
Mostraua toda aquella sal, de gruesso,
Vna muy larga pica bien tendida.[7]

1604.—Oñate mentions deposits, in the province of Zuni, of a blue "silver" (azurite) used as pigment, and also deposits, in the Jemez country, of a green mineral (malachite). (Bolton, 1916, p. 269.)

1610.—Santa Fe, the new capital, was founded by Governor don Pedro de Peralta.

1620–26.—Assays of silver ores were made during this period (Ayer, 1916, p. 218).

6. *Traslado de la informacion del descubrimiento de las salinas de Zuñi,* Nov. 8, 1598: Archivo General de Indias, Patronato, leg. 22. I am indebted to France V. Scholes for this reference, and to Eleanor B. Adams for the translation.

7. *Historia de la Nueva México por el Capitán Gaspar de Villagrá* (reimpresa por el Museo Nacional de México), México, 1900, tomo 1, p. 102. Translation by Eleanor B. Adams:

"And they immediately ordered Captain Farfán to go to discover certain salt beds concerning which important information had been received. And, executing that order with great promptness and care, he soon returned and reported that they were so rich and large that for a distance of a long league all that salt was apparently as thick as the full length of a very long pike."

1629.—Fray Gerónimo de Zárate Salmerón worked in New Mexico during the period 1621–26. In his *Relaciones,* compiled in 1629, he mentions numerous ore deposits and states that he has "seen silver, copper, lead, loadstone, copperas, alum, sulfur, and mines of turquois." He cites also the salt lakes and the garnet deposits near Picuris Pueblo. Salmerón might be considered the first enthusiastic promoter in the history of the United States. Witness the following statement:

> "In all the ranges of the Hemex [Jemez] there is nothing but deposits, where I discovered many and filed on them for His Majesty. From the which I took out eighteen arrobas [1 arroba = 25.317 lbs. av.] of ore. As I returned [to Mexico] I distributed these ores at all the mining-camps I passed in order that all might see the ores of New Mexico. Before all things, there are mineral deposits, and there is no corner which has them not." (Translation by F. W. Hodge, in Ayer, 1916, p. 217.)

1630.—Fray Alonso de Benavides, in his *Memorial,* has a section entitled "Mines of Socorro." He notes the existence of "very great treasures of mines,[8] very rich and prosperous in silver and gold," especially in the Socorro region, and says he made numerous assays. He mentions the Estancia salt lakes, the deposits "of very fine garnets" at Picuris Pueblo, the turquois mines worked by the Indians, and the abundance of rock alum in the Gila-Navajo region; this alum was used by the Indians in dyeing cloth (Ayer, 1916, p. 18–44).

1660.—Salt from the Estancia salt lakes was being transported 700 miles to the silver mines in southern Chihuahua, Mexico (Scholes, 1942, p. 29, 44, 48).

1680.—The Pueblo Revolt. The Indians revolted and drove out the Spaniards; prospecting and mining ceased almost entirely for a period of many years. Some writers have held that this revolt was caused at least in part by the enslavement of the Indians in mining, but most writers deny this and claim that there was very little exploitation of mineral deposits, except salt and turquois, prior to 1680. Scholes (1935, p. 79), for example, states that "there is no evidence that mining was successfully carried on, even on a minor scale" during the 17th century. In view of such a strong statement, some of the contradictory evidence is presented.

F. A. Jones (1904, p. 13) concluded that, with the exception of "Mina del Tierra" (also called "Mina del Tero," "Mina del Tiro," etc.) in the Cerrillos district, little true metal mining was carried on prior to 1800. In a lengthy footnote Jones stated:

8. Although Bandelier (1892, p. 94) called attention long ago to the fact that the word "minas," in older Spanish, was used to designate simply mineral deposits or localities where minerals were found, and not *worked* mines, in the English sense, many historians have been given to translating the word "minas" as "mines." The erroneous translation of this one word has undoubtedly contributed greatly to the search for mineral wealth and to the development of New Mexico's mineral industry!

"The uprising of the Pueblo Indians in 1680 was said to have been due to the hardships of slavery inflicted on those people by the Spaniards, principally in working the mines. Be this as it may, history tells us that the Spaniards had to flee the country as a result of their extreme cruelty and barbarity. . . .

"It seems that the Jesuits were, formerly, the principal miners before the revolt of 1680, and they were the ones on whom the Pueblos mainly wreaked their vengeance in a general massacre.

"Tradition has it that all the known mines at that time were filled in and so completely covered up, that when the Spaniards returned and who were prohibited from doing mining, the succeeding generations were unable to discover the mines again. During the temporary exodus of the Spaniard from the country [1680 to 1692], the records were either destroyed by the Pueblos or were carried to Mexico and Spain by the fugitives in their flight, resulting in the complete obliteration of all the early mines and mining records of the country.

"From all the evidence obtainable on the early Spanish mines, we are forced to the conclusion that the mining in that day was scarcely removed from what we now term prospecting."

Jones (op. cit., p. 14) also observed that

"The Spaniard has been a gold hunter from the earliest times and placer gold was the kind he knew most about; lode mines were not so alluring to him."

C. W. Henderson (1933, p. 731) wrote:

"With the history of mining in Colorado, New Mexico, and Arizona from 1845 to 1932 well in mind, and recognizing the remarkable ability of the Mexican as a prospector and the enormous early production of Mexico, the writer has reached the conclusion that Spaniards and Mexicans did no mining in Colorado, very little in California, but some in New Mexico, and doubtless some in Arizona."

Brief résumés of evidences of Spanish mining operations are given here, arranged in order from northern to southern New Mexico.

Taos County.—Prior to 1680, the Spaniards are reported to have operated mines in Taos County for gold, silver, and copper with Indian labor. It was rumored that

"The Franciscan Fathers, working in the name of the church, are said to have taken out several million dollars in this way."

Again, we read that

". . . millions in gold and silver were taken out of the mines in the Taos mountains near Arroyo Hondo, and that the Spaniards concealed a hoard of $14,000,000 in one shaft before fleeing" in 1680. Following the Reconquest in 1692, gold mines were again worked by the Spaniards (Anonymous, 1901a, p. 5–6).

A news item (*Mining World,* Las Vegas, v. 3, no. 3, Oct. 1, 1882, p. 35) states:

> "In the records of the old church at Taos, New Mexico, it is shown that $10,000,000 was collected by priests as tithes from a single mine in the Taos mountains. . . ."

Santa Fe County.—Wislizenus (1848) stated that several rich silver mines were worked in Spanish times "at Cerrillos, and in the Nambe mountains, but none at present." In the Cerrillos district,

> ". . . the water as well as the ore had to be conveyed to the surface upon the backs of peons who climbed from terrace to terrace upon notched logs" (*Mining World,* Las Vegas, v. 2, no. 9, Jan. 16, 1882, p. 154).

The estimated Spanish production of the Cerrillos district was more than $3,000,000 to the church and, in addition to this, they "filled the coffers of their king" (*Mining World,* Las Vegas, v. 2, no. 19, July 15, 1882, p. 260). A single mine, the Mina del Tero (Tiro), paid in tithes "to the Catholic Church of Spain" more than $300,000 at a depth of 100 feet. Another mine, the Rue Alevia, paid $237,000 to the Church of Spain in three months (*Mining World,* Las Vegas, v. 3, no. 6, Dec. 1, 1882, p. 88).

In the Old Placers district,

> "In 1680 the Ortiz mine . . . was a famous gold producer. Here the Pueblo Indians . . . were made to do almost superhuman tasks, climbing notched poles, which answered as ladders, with their burdens of gold-bearing ores" (Anonymous, 1901a, p. 56).

The placers here and in the New Placers district were operated only with the greatest difficulty. Water had to be packed in on burros for many miles during the dry season and, in winter, snow was often melted with heated rocks. Referring to the New Placers district, Howe (1881) stated that

> "In former years the dirt was carried to the Rio Grande on burros and there washed. The dirt is so rich that even this expensive method was profitable."

Bernalillo County.—In his report on the mines and mining of Bernalillo County, Howe (1881) wrote:

> "Numerous ruins of smelters are also found, giving indisputable evidence that mines were once worked on a large scale. Two hundred years ago the Indians, who had been enslaved and forced to work these mines broke out in rebellion and drove the Spaniards from the country. So intense was their hatred toward those places in which they had been forced to labor, that they filled up every old mine so that no trace could

be found of them. A number of years after the Spaniards were allowed to return. . . ."

More specific citations are certain news items such as this:

> "An old mine has been discovered in the Tijeras canyon, with a tunnel 75 feet in. Tools of the old Spanish pattern were found in the tunnel" (*Mining World,* Las Vegas, v. 1, no. 11, July, 1881).

Ruins of ancient smelters were reported at many places in the Sandia Mountains and "much of the slag now found near these old smelters contains gold in considerable quantities" (*Mining World,* Las Vegas, v. 2, no. 9 [10], Jan. 16 [Feb. 20], 1882, p. 169).

According to Burke (1896, p. 24),

> "The Longfellow mine, between Tijeras and Coyote cañons, is an old Spanish working from which great quantities of copper were produced in the early days of Spanish occupancy. Old copper vessels and implements made from this ore are found occasionally, and the old workings show that much ore has been mined here."

For the later history of this mine, see under date 1840.

Torrance County.—In an article describing the silver, copper, and lead ores of the southwest slope of the Manzano Mountains, one writer (Anonymous, 1880b) stated that

> "The oldest inhabitant of Abo has no recollections or traditions of mining being done there, but the ruins of twenty-two smelters or furnaces which they [two prospectors] discovered attest that it at one time was the seat of extensive mineral works. The slag shows silver to be the principal mineral which had been worked and pieces of pure silver can be picked up in the vicinity of the ancient furnaces."

Socorro County.—There are several references, chiefly news items (*Mining World,* Las Vegas, 1880 to 1884), to old Spanish workings at Socorro Peak. In the old St. Felicite district, an ancient smelter and two old mines were found. "Recovered Spanish workings" were reported in the Ladron district. In the Council Rock district, formerly Iron Mountain No. 1, Spanish smelters were found near the Old Boss mine; the slag yielded both gold and silver.

Sierra County.—According to Leeson (1896, p. 41, 43), the earliest mining in what was then Socorro County (now Sierra) was in 1655 in the Goodfortune Creek district by "a noted Spanish explorer named Marguerito Luero." Later he stated that the mine was "discovered in 1655 by one of the followers of that noted priest, missionary and explorer, Father Guerra. . . ." It was reported that many rich shipments of gold were made from this mine until 1712. The mine then appears to have become lost for more than a century. It was rediscovered by Dr. C. F. Blackington, who named it the Good Fortune.

Lincoln County.—In the Estey district, wire gold and wire silver were found in an old shaft reported to have been worked hundreds of years ago (*Mining World,* Las Vegas, v. 1, no. 6, Feb., 1881, p. 12).

Dona Ana County.—Old workings and ruins of smelters used by the ancient Spanish were reported in 1883 at the Modoc mine (Anonymous, 1883). According to Dunham (1935, p. 188):

> "It is said that in the late years of the Spanish occupation of New Mexico, a priest named LaRue, stationed at a hacienda in Chihuahua [Mexico], was told by a dying friend of placers and a fabulously rich gold-bearing lode in the mountains two days' journey north of Paso del Norte [El Paso]. When drought brought a famine to the community of peons in his charge at the hacienda, Father LaRue persuaded them to migrate northward with him, the Organ Mountains being his goal. Arrived here, the priest recognized landmarks which had been described to him, and, sending his men out to search, succeeded in finding the rich deposits. The colony settled at Spirit Springs (now the Cox ranch) and here the gold was concentrated in arrastres, and some of the ore was smelted in "vassos" (adobe furnaces). The mine is supposed to have been located in a deep canyon west or southwest of the springs. The long silence of the priest led the authorities of the Church in the City of Mexico to send an expedition to his former place of labor; finding this deserted, they traced him to the Organ Mountains. Learning from his guards that the expedition was approaching, LaRue gave orders that the mine was to be covered up and the gold hidden. When the expedition arrived, he refused to divulge the secret of the whereabouts of the mine and gold, asserting that they belonged to his people and not to the Church. By night he was murdered by a soldier attached to the expedition, and afterwards some of the colonists were tortured, but the secret was never told. The mine is supposed to have been covered up by debris from the mountains."

1685.—On March 26, the first mining claim was filed before Don Domingo Jironza Petríz de Cruzate, governor and captain-general, by Pedro de Abalos for his mine, Nuestra Señora del Pilar de Zaragoza, in the Fray Cristobal Mountains (Twitchell, 1914, v. 1, p. 1, archive no. 1).

1692.—September. Reconquest by Governor don Diego de Vargas Zapata Lujan Ponce de Leon, who wrote a report to the viceroy in which he recommended "the sending of convict mechanics from Mexican jails to serve as teachers and search for metals" (Bancroft, 1888, p. 200).

1694.—Capt. Madrid attempted to get lead for bullets from a lead mine that had been worked by his father near Cerrillos but found that the Indians had filled it up (Bancroft, 1888, p. 207).

1697.—Fray Agustín de Vetancurt, in his *Crónica de la provincia del Santo Evangelio de México,* wrote:

"There are deposits of silver, copper, jet, lodestone, and one of transparent talc-like gypsum which they extract in sheets and adorn windows with them as if they were of glass" (Vetancurt, 1871, p. 297; translation by F. V. Scholes).

Referring specifically to San Marcos (Cerrillos), he wrote:

"Nearby there is a bald and rocky mountain where there are found ores [or veins] of lead and silver, and where they extract turquois, and a vein of lodestone, and where they take out gypsum as transparent as crystal [or glass]" (Vetancurt, 1871, p. 324).

Vetancurt (1871, p. 325) described the Estancia salt lakes as follows:

"San Gregorio Abbo is located in the valley of the salinas where, within an area ten leagues in circumference, all the rain water is converted into hard salt which they take out in blocks and transport to all parts of the Custodia and even to the mines of Parral [in Mexico]."

1709–10.—Two mines were registered by Juan de Uribarri before the governor, Admiral don José Chacón, Marqués de las Peñuelas (Twitchell, 1914, v. 1, p. 299, archives nos. 1018 and 1019).

1713.—A mine in Rio Arriba County was registered before Gov. don Juan Ignacio Flores Mogollón. According to F. A. Jones (1904, p. 13),

". . . in the archives at Santa Fe, under date of 1713, is the document of *Nuestra Sra. de los Reyes de Linares,* which refers to an old covered up mine in *Sierra de San Lazora,* (Old Placer Mountain). And in 1714 a gift of the whole or part of this same mine was made."

1717.—Grant of a lead mine in the Cerrillos district was made to Diego Arias de Quirós by Gov. don Juan Paez Hurtado.

1722.—Gold was mined at La Mina de la Tierra (or Tiro), in the Cerrillos district.

1744.—Several mines near Picuris Pueblo were registered before Gov. don Joaquín Codallos y Rabal.

1790.—Population of New Mexico: 30,953.

1800.—The Santa Rita copper deposit was shown by a friendly Apache chief to Lieut.-Col. José Manuel Carrasco (Carasco, Carisco, or Carrisco), who was in charge of the Spanish military posts in New Mexico. Carrasco interested Don Manuel Francisco Elguea, of Chihuahua, in the property.

1804.—Elguea purchased Carrasco's interests in the Santa Rita property and began mining copper. The copper was transported by mule trains under military convoy to Chihuahua and to Mexico City, where it was used chiefly for coinage. It is said that the mine produced 20,000 mule loads of copper annually.

1807.—Lieut. Zebulon M. Pike and party were arrested and taken first to Santa Fe and thence to Mexico. Pike noted that a "flexible talc" was used for windows in most of the houses at Santa Fe. Bancroft claimed that this was not talc but gypsum. I believe that it was neither talc nor gypsum, but mica. Apparently, mica was used extensively in Santa Fe whereas gypsum was used in many other towns.[9] Pike cited also salt, copper, and gold.

NEW MEXICO UNDER THE REPUBLIC OF MEXICO

1821.—New Mexico became a province of Mexico.

1824.—New Mexico became a territory of Mexico. The Santa Fe trail was established; traders are reported to have returned to Missouri this year with $180,000 in gold and silver.

1825.—Samuel Robinson's *A catalogue of American minerals, with their localities* cites minerals from a total of 27 states, the District of Columbia, Labrador, New Brunswick, Nova Scotia, Lower Canada (Quebec), and Upper Canada (Ontario). It is interesting to note that the westernmost parts of the United States included in the catalogue are Illinois, Missouri, Arkansas, and Louisiana.

1827.—Population of Albuquerque: 2,547; Taos: 3,606, Abiquiu: 3,557, and Santa Fe: 5,759 (Coan, 1925, p. 325).

1828.—Placer gold was discovered by a sheepherder at the Old Placers, in the Ortiz Mountains between Albuquerque and Santa Fe. This is regarded as the first important discovery of gold west of the Mississippi River. According to F. A. Jones (1908b), it took three months for news of the discovery to reach the banks of the Missouri River, only 800 miles away.

> "The discovery was made late in the winter, and the plowing season in the east was in full swing, when the news became generally known.
>
> "Excitement ran high and the first epidemic of 'gold fever' had the country in its grasp. The mad rush was on and nothing could check its momentum. Plows that were active as of today, stood in the furrow on the morrow motionless as a corpse. Fields of growing corn and waving grain were abandoned and given over to the weeds and wind.
>
> "[This discovery] is considered the first call in the awakening of the west. . . .
>
> "It was then that the first organized assault on the store houses of

9. More than a century ago J. D. Dana (1837, p. 264) wrote:

"When quite thin, the laminae of mica are often transparent, and have been used in Siberia for windows. It is hence sometimes called Muscovy glass. It however soon loses its transparency on exposure, and is but a poor substitute for the valuable product of art in general use. It is also used on board the Russian naval vessels, as it is less liable to fracture with the concussion produced by the discharge of heavy artillery."

wealth of the Rocky Mountains was made, and the line of march definitely marked out the famous Santa Fe Trail."

1832–35.—According to Gregg (1844), "the quantity of gold extracted between the years 1832 and '35 could not have amounted to less than from $60,000 to $80,000 per annum."

1833.—Gold-quartz veins were discovered near the Old Placers. On Dec. 18, the Santa Rosalia grant was recorded in favor of José Francisco Ortiz, in the Sierra de Oro, west of Mina del Compromiso. On Dec. 19, a record was made of a mine adjoining the Ortiz mine.

1836.—The territory of New Mexico became a department.

1837.—The first edition of James Dwight Dana's *A system of mineralogy* cited minerals from those states lying east of the Mississippi River and from Arkansas and Missouri, as well as Mexico, but not from New Mexico. It should be noted further that Dana's (op. cit., appendix, p. 94–106) bibliography of the American literature on mineralogy includes few articles published prior to 1800.

1839.—The New Placers district was discovered in the San Pedro Mountains.

1840.—In a description of the mines of Bernalillo County, one author (Anonymous, 1906, p. 11) stated that

> "About two miles from the Placita of Tijeras, on the eastern slope of the Sandias, is the Longfellow mine. . . . It was discovered in 1840 and was operated by a Frenchman who reduced the ore to matte in a small adobe furnace. The metal produced by this furnace was used in casting many of the church bells for small towns in this portion of New Mexico. The remainder of the product was shipped east by pack train. The owner, by getting into trouble with the native populace, was forced to leave the country. Some time later the mine was again worked by a party from Chihuahua, Mexico, who shipped part of the ore east, but most of it went to Chihuahua. In 1863 the mine passed into the hands of a Las Vegas merchant, who, after a small amount of development work, encountered a large body of copper glance. He made no attempt to treat the ore, but sent it by ox-team to Kansas City, whence it was shipped to the Atlantic Coast, the first shipment being to Baltimore, Maryland, and later shipments to Newark, New Jersey. His last shipment of three six-mule team-loads netted a profit of $8,000. The ore was a high-grade copper glance with yellow and red oxide and argentite. The gold values in the ore alone paid all cost of production, transportation and treatment. In 1882 a contract was let to clean out the old shaft and retimber the mine. A body of ore blocked out in 1863 was taken out, part being treated at San Pedro, Santa Fe County, and the rest was sacked and shipped east. An epidemic of smallpox among the miners resulted in

the closing of the mine. Once more, in 1891–2, work was commenced under contract."

1841.—Thomas Falconer, a Fellow of the Geological Society of London, was in New Mexico but had little opportunity to make geologic observations. He was a member of the ill-fated Texan–Santa Fe expedition. Members of the party were arrested and Falconer's notes and mineral collection were seized. En route to Mexico as a prisoner, Falconer observed salt somewhere near Socorro and "mica" used for windows at Socorro. (This mineral was undoubtedly selenite, not mica.)

1843.—Golden is reported to have

". . . had a population of 5,000, who worked the mines known as the New Placers. Large nuggets were sometimes found, the largest one of seven pounds" (*Mining World,* Las Vegas, v. 2, no. 9, Jan. 16, 1882, p. 152).

1844.—Josiah Gregg, most famous of all the Santa Fe traders, devoted a chapter of his *Commerce of the Prairies* to the mines of New Mexico. He stated that the only successful mines were those of gold and cited ores of several metals, the salt at Estancia, beautiful specimens of petrified wood near Cerrillos, and the use of selenite for windowpanes.

1845.—The value of gold produced this year from the Old and New Placers was $250,000. According to Meline (1873), at the Old Placers, "many large lumps, or nuggets, were obtained, some worth $500, $700, $1500, and one, in particular, of $3400, which its finder sold for $1400." At the New Placers, Tuerto (present village of Golden) "had in it more than a hundred houses, and twenty-two stores transacting more business than was done in Santa Fe."

AMERICAN OCCUPATION—NEW MEXICO A TERRITORY OF THE UNITED STATES

1846.—May 13: War between the United States and Mexico. Sept. 22: Proclamation of provisional government by Brig.-Gen. Stephen W. Kearny. The Santo Niño mine, north of the Ortiz mine, was recorded (Old Placers district). A mine was recorded in the "Real San Francisco del Tuerto" (New Placers district). Geological observations were made this year by three different men engaged in military reconnaissance: F. A. Wislizenus, W. H. Emory, and J. W. Abert.

Dr. Wislizenus explored the territory in June, July, and Aug., 1846. He entered at the northeastern corner, traveled through Las Vegas to Santa Fe, visited the Old and New Placers, passed through Albuquerque, and went south to El Paso. In his *Memoir of a tour to northern Mexico, connected with Col. Doniphan's expedition, in 1846 and 1847,* published in 1848, he cited nine species of minerals from New Mexico and gave an analysis of placer gold. He (op. cit., p. 24) wrote:

> "A third, much neglected branch of industry in New Mexico are the *mines*. Great many now deserted mining places in New Mexico prove that mining was pursued with greater zeal in the old Spanish times than at present, which may be accounted for in various ways, as the present want of capital, want of knowledge in mining, but especially the unsettled state of the country and the avarice of its arbitrary rulers. The mountainous parts of New Mexico are very rich in gold, copper, iron, and some silver."

Lieut. Emory was in New Mexico during Aug., Sept., and Oct., 1846. He entered near Raton and went southward through Socorro to Hot Springs (Truth or Consequences); somewhere south of here he left the Rio Grande and headed westward toward Cooks Pass, crossed the Mimbres and Gila Rivers, and went on into Arizona. In his *Notes of a military reconnoissance from Fort Leavenworth, in Missouri, to San Diego, in California*, published in 1848, he cited 11 species of minerals from New Mexico.

Lieut. Abert was in New Mexico between Sept., 1846, and Jan., 1847. He also entered at Raton, traveled to Santa Fe and both Old and New Placers, crossed the Rio Puerco, visited Acoma, and returned to the Rio Grande and the Manzano Mountains; thence he went south to Socorro and finally returned to Raton. In his report, published in 1848, he cited several minerals. His specimens were later submitted to J. W. Bailey, professor of chemistry, mineralogy, and geology at West Point; Bailey's notes accompanied Abert's report. Together, Abert and Bailey cited 11 minerals from New Mexico.

1847.—Referring to the Coyote Creek district of Mora County, Hadley (1881) stated that about 1847 a Frenchman "maintained himself by mining the copper ores upon a small scale." He added that the metal for the bell in the church at Taos was mined in the "Cayote" Mountains of Mora County. (It is likely that Hadley confused the Coyote Basin–Coyote Canyon–Tijeras Canyon district of Bernalillo County with the Coyote Creek district of Mora County. See under date of 1840.)

1848.—The Treaty of Guadalupe Hidalgo was signed.

1849.—Lieut. J. H. Simpson was in northwestern New Mexico on military reconnaissance. On Aug. 20 he visited an abandoned "copper-smelting furnace" near Jemez Springs and "picked up some fragments of copper ore (probably green malachite) which lay scattered around." On Aug. 26, near Cabezon, in the valley of the Rio Puerco, he

> ". . . found some beautiful specimens of petrified wood—in two instances the trunks of the trees still standing erect and *in situ*. One of

these trunks was two feet high by two in diameter, and the other three feet high by two and a half in diameter."

Simpson's report, published in 1850, contained two color plates illustrating this petrified wood; these plates bear the notation: "Printed in colours at P. S. Duval's Steam lith. Press Establ. Phila." (These plates appear to constitute the earliest illustration of any New Mexico mineral.)

Capt. R. B. Marcy was in the territory on military reconnaissance from Fort Smith to Santa Fe; only two minerals were cited in his report. Lead ores, notably the Stevenson lode, were discovered in the Organ Mountains.

1850.—On Sept. 9 New Mexico became a territory of the United States with full civil government. Placer gold was found near Jicarilla.

1853–56.—In 1853 the Congress authorized explorations for a railroad route to the Pacific. Several parties were sent out in the spring of 1853 by the Secretary of War, Jefferson Davis. Explorations were carried on in New Mexico by Marcou, Blake, Antisell, and others. Several volumes of reports were published, bearing the general title:

> "Reports of explorations and surveys, to ascertain the most practicable and economical route for a railroad from the Mississippi River to the Pacific Ocean; Made under the direction of the Secretary of War, in 1853-6, according to Acts of Congress. . . ."

The Swiss geologist, Jules Marcou, accompanied Lieut. Whipple on the expedition along the 35th parallel as geologist and mining engineer. His original field notes in French are given in the left-hand column and a translation by W. P. Blake is given in the right-hand column. See Marcou (1856) and Blake (1856a). Marcou was more interested in fossils and stratigraphy than in mineralogy but he mentioned a few minerals.

W. P. Blake, in his report on the route near the 35th parallel, cited 18 species of minerals. In another short report on a portion of the route near the 32d parallel, Blake gave partial analyses of galena and of cerussite from the Organ Mountains. Thomas Antisell, in his report on the route near the 32d parallel, cited 18 species of minerals and gave two analyses of argentiferous galena from the Organ Mountains.

1854.—Agatized wood collected by Dr. Baldwin Möllhausen in the valley of Rio Seco was studied in Berlin by Göppert, who named the tree *Araucarites möllhausianus.*

1858.—Prof. J. S. Newberry was attached to Lieut. J. C. Ives' expedition up the Colorado River. Newberry reported briefly on the geology of the route from Fort Defiance to Santa Fe, Las Vegas, and Raton. He cited 12 minerals from New Mexico. It may be noted that he mistook the peridots of the Fort Defiance area for beryls. The first technical description of any length of a New Mexico mineral was that by W. P. Blake of the turquois at Cerrillos.

1859.—Capt. J. N. Macomb and Prof. Newberry were in northwestern New Mexico on military reconnaissance. Newberry's report, not published until 1876, cited 10 species of minerals.

1860.—Gold placers were discovered at Pinos Altos in May; lode gold was discovered in Dec., by which time 1,500 persons were present. Rich gold placers were reported near Fort Stanton. The census report of this year mentions three copper mines and one silver mine in Dona Ana County, employing 390 men and producing $212,000 (Bancroft, 1888, p. 649). The Hanover mine in Grant County shipped copper to the Texas coast during the period 1858–61.

1861.—The Civil War began.

1862.—Mining was suspended during the Confederate invasion. There were numerous Indian raids this year.

1863.—The first important discovery of silver in New Mexico was made at Pueblo Springs, near Magdalena, by Pete Kinsinger, a soldier.

1865.—The Civil War ended. Gold was discovered near Nogal. Many changes were made in the political subdivisions of New Mexico between 1865 and 1880. New counties were established as mining developments demanded. In their *Report on the mines of New Mexico,*[10] Prof. R. E. Owen and E. T. Cox cited a total of 23 species and several additional varieties of minerals, and gave several analyses of minerals and ores. As an example of the latter, their analysis of copper ore from the St. Adelia silver mines in the Organ Mountains is given here:

Moisture dried at 300° F.	00.100
Silicates	40.400
Oxide of Copper	31.347
Oxide of Lead	09.832
Iron and Alumina	05.000
Carbonic Acid	07.000
Sulphuric Acid	.100
Selenious Acid and undt. substances and loss	00.221
	[94.000]

Owen and Cox (op. cit., p. 27-28) were much impressed by

". . . the ants, which raise from beneath the soil small gravel in hillocks, sometimes 2 feet high and 6 feet in diameter, and when permitted inad-

10. In the Introduction to the 1942 edition of *Minerals of New Mexico,* I commented: "A few of the older papers have not been seen. For example, the writer was unable to locate a copy of the fifty-nine page 'Report on the Mines of New Mexico,' published in 1865 by Richard Owen and E. T. Cox. (The Library of Congress reported that the only copy cited in its files was one ascribed to the Princeton University Library and the latter could not find it.)" Upon reading this statement, Senator Clinton P. Anderson kindly loaned me a copy from his personal library.

vertently to get over the shoe on foot, bite the human limb to a painful extent."

1866.—Lead-silver ores were found at Magdalena by J. S. Hutchason ("Old Hutch"). Silver ore was discovered at Georgetown, and placer gold in the Moreno Valley. According to Anonymous (1910d), the latter discovery

> ". . . resulted in a stampede which increased the population of Elizabethtown to 10,000, made it the first incorporated city in New Mexico, and for a time the county seat of Colfax county which had then just been organized. It is estimated that more than 2½ millions of dollars in gold have come from the placer fields around Mt. Baldy."

(I doubt that E-town ever had a population of 10,000. See other figures of 5,000–7,000.)

1867.—The Elizabethtown boom began. Gold was found near Taos, and it was reported that 400 men were at work here. Silver ore was discovered at Socorro Peak. Bullion from the Graphic and Juanita claims at Magdalena was hauled by wagons over the Santa Fe trail to St. Louis. New Mexico's first stamp mills were built at Pinos Altos and at the Ortiz mine. In his report as "Special Commissioner for the collection of statistics upon gold and silver mining east of the Rocky mountains," James W. Taylor (1867, p. 324–326) observed that

> "At this time Indian hostilities prevent permanent labor, and almost exploration, in the remote districts of New Mexico. . . .
>
> ". . . the second annual message of acting Governor Arny, delivered in December, 1866 . . . reports the discovery of thirty lodes of gold-bearing quartz at Pinos Altos, paying from $40 to $200 per ton. . . .
>
> ". . . silver is the prominent and most abundant mineral of the Territory. . . . In the Organ mountains over fifty silver mines have been discovered, the ore being generally argentiferous galena.
>
> "Governor Arny . . . observes of the production of copper, that, before the late civil war, two copper mines were extensively worked—the Santa Rita and the Hanover—turning out about twelve tons of copper per week, and employing jointly about five hundred hands. . . .
>
> "A copper mine has lately been discovered a short distance from Fort Union. . . ."

1868.—Taylor's report for this year also mentions many ore deposits in New Mexico but cites few minerals. He writes:

> "For many years much of the copper ore of New Mexico has been transported to Indianola, Texas, a distance of 1,000 miles, and the amount of gold associated with the copper has always been sufficient to defray the expenses of transportation."

The Ladron and Water Canyon districts were discovered. Grant County was established and named for Gen. U. S. Grant.

1868–69.—In his report on mining districts from the Sandia Mountains northward to Colorado, Persifor Frazer, Jr., cited 45 minerals. The Big Ditch, 41 miles long, was constructed to bring water from Red River to Elizabethtown for placer mining. Lindgren, Graton, and Gordon (1910, p. 93) commented that the Big Ditch, "built at a cost of over $200,000 . . . has stood as a monument to the energy of those early prospectors." Population of E-town: 5,000. The Aztec lode "was said to have been the richest discovery made in the west, of gold from a vein or lode" (Jones, F. A., 1904, p. 149).

1869.—Colfax and Lincoln Counties were established. Elizabethtown, with a population of possibly 7,000, was made the county seat of Colfax County. First newpaper in Colfax County: *The Lantern.*

1870.—Population of New Mexico: 91,874. Numerous mining districts were mentioned by R. W. Raymond in his report on mines and mining west of the Rocky Mountains and 38 minerals were cited from New Mexico. Prospecting began at Lordsburg.

1871.—The rich silver ores at Chloride Flat were discovered and gave Silver City its name. Over $3,000,000 in silver was obtained in a short time, and the total production from 1871 to 1893 has been estimated as high as $5,000,000. The Lone Mountain district was discovered and the Burro Mountains were prospected.

1872.—Prospecting was carried on in the Hansonburg area.

1873.—First newspaper at Silver City: *Mining Life.* Oscar Loew, in his report of work done for the Wheeler Survey (published 1875), cited 48 minerals from New Mexico. He also gave analyses of alunogen, halite, and trona, and described a new species of resin—wheelerite.

1874.—In his report (published 1875) of work done this year, Loew cited 26 species and gave analyses of chabazite, pyrope garnet, olivine, and turquois.

1875.—The Mogollon and Steins Pass districts were prospected.

1876.—Ore was discovered in the Cooks Peak region.

1877.—Placers and gold lodes were found at Hillsboro.

1878.—The first railroad track in New Mexico was laid on Nov. 30. Silver ores were discovered at Lake Valley in Aug. This district yielded 5,000,000 ounces of silver within a few years. The Bridal Chamber, discovered in the early 80's, was one of the richest bodies of silver ore in the world. (See under 1884.) According to F. A. Jones (1908c), prehistoric turquois workings were found at and near the mining camp of Old Hachita.

> "The prospectors, elated over such an extraordinary discovery, called the district 'Eureka.' . . .

"In these old dumps and pits were found fragments of the most ancient kind of pottery, as well as crude stone hammers and other implements, indicating the stone age, furnishing conclusive proof of the antiquity of the workings."

1879.—Modoc was located, Wilcox was discovered, and Orogrande was prospected. Silver ores were found at Chloride. At Cerrillos, zinc-lead-silver ores were discovered and a boom started; more than 1,000 locations were made here within a short time. According to Howard Bryan, in his column, "Off the beaten path" (*Albuquerque Tribune*, April 23, 1956),

"The history of White Oaks dates back to 1879 when a small group of prospectors entered the valley and began panning gold in paying quantities.

"The prospectors included John J. Baxter, John V. (Uncle Jack) Winters and John E. Wilson, who spent the summer washing gold out of the small stream which became known as Baxter's Gulch.

"The prospectors were joined later by an old Arizona prospector named Tom Wilson. . . .

"While prospecting at the head of the gulch one day, Tom sat down on a large boulder to rest. Noticing some crystals on the corner of the boulder, he broke them open with his pick and found particles of wire gold inside.

"The two partners [Tom Wilson and Winters] staked out a claim on the site which they called the Homestake. The Arizona prospector left shortly after the strike, accepting $40 in gold washings, two dollars in silver and an old pistol for his share of the claim, which later was sold for $300,000. . . .

"That winter the famous Old Abe claim was discovered, which was to yield $3,000,000 in gold over the years from the deepest dry shaft in the nation."

The Old Abe mine was 1,375 feet deep.

1879–82.—The construction of the Southern Pacific Railroad and the Atchison, Topeka and Santa Fe Railway, according to Lindgren, Graton, and Gordon (1910, p. 18),

". . . brought a large number of prospectors and miners. This was a period of great activity. Practically all the mining districts now [1910] worked were then discovered and developed."

Metzger (1938, p. 7–8) notes that "many of the soldiers detailed to guard the railroad construction gangs and the overland stage routes spent much of their leisure time in prospecting and discovered some important deposits."

Track was laid into Las Vegas on July 1, 1879; it was extended to Santa Fe on Feb. 9, 1880, and to Albuquerque on April 22. According to Coan (1925, p. 451-452),

"Mining in New Mexico rapidly became an important industry and source of wealth between 1879 and 1911. Before 1879 gold was the principal mineral. After 1879 silver was found in much larger quantities than gold."

Copper mining did not really become profitable until railroad transportation was available.

1880.—Population of New Mexico: 119,565. Cochiti, Cooks Peak, and Steeple Rock districts were prospected. Eureka and Fremont districts were discovered. A number of miners were killed in the Mogollon district by Apaches led by Victorio. The principal period of activity in the Victorio district was 1880–86. Rich silver ores were found at Kingston and within five years the population increased to about 6,000; at one time there were 22 saloons and 3 newspapers. According to Howard Bryan (*Albuquerque Tribune,* April 23, 1956),

"The town of White Oaks was staked out in the spring of 1880, and by the end of that year it contained dozens of flourishing businesses including mercantile stores, saloons, drug stores, gambling halls, an opera house, a bank and a newspaper called The Golden Era.

"Proprietors of the Pioneer Saloon sold three different grades of whisky at three different prices—all of it taken from the same barrel."

In Sept. a monthly paper, the *Mining World,* was started in Las Vegas; publication continued until Dec., 1885. The banner across the first page of most numbers was a quotation: " 'The wealth of the world will be found in New Mexico and Arizona.'—Baron Alexander Von Humboldt." Most of the following items for 1880–83 are culled from this mining paper.

Gen. and Mrs. U. S. Grant visited the New Placers district in July. Grant was elected president of the San Pedro and Cañon de L'Agua Company. It was reported that $800,000 was paid for the San Pedro property.

"Some large nuggets have been taken out, and Grant, who recently went to New Mexico to take a look at the place, is credited with expressing his belief that there is a good deal of money there if worked the right way. The great drawback is a scarcity of water. If this can be obtained it is said the placers can be worked profitably, and Gen. Grant has an idea that pipes can be laid from the Sandia mountains and sufficient water obtained" (*Mining World,* Las Vegas, v. 1, no. 1, Sept., 1880, p. 4).

About 1,200 locations were made at White Oaks; one assay here was reported to run $18,000 per ton in gold. Ore assaying $600 in silver was found in the Ladron district. At the Placitas district of the northern Sandias, 150 persons were in camp; the first assay from the Lida lode ran $4,604 in gold; the old Montezuma mine was bought by New York parties for $60,000. According to Hadley (1881), who was describing the copper-silver ores from the Bessie claim of the Coyote Creek district of Mora County:

> "A mill run in Baltimore a year ago returned $165.50 to the owners for two tons after paying twenty cents per hundred for shipping. . . . It is an interesting fact that this ore is found with a hard bituminous coal, in which we found upon test a considerable amount of copper."

Gold and silver were reported (Anonymous, 1880a) in the Mora area; silver and copper in the Turkey Mountains, northeast of Fort Union, and also in Apache Hill on the stage route north of Fort Union; and silver near the Hot Springs, 6 miles northwest of Las Vegas. "At Tecolote, about twelve miles South of Las Vegas, a mining camp has lately sprung up, and rich developments of silver are made there." Also, "exceedingly rich ore of silver" was reported in the Jicarilla district. More than the usual number of typographical errors are to be found in a story by Kernal (1880) on the Socorro area, especially the elusive St. Felicite district:

> "F. Manzanares has several fine old claims there which are 300 years old. . . . The La Plata shows a face of argentiferous galena and chloride of sliver [sic] in a gangue of flour [sic] spar and sulphate of barata [sic] six feet four inches wide, and ten feet of quartz bearing silver."

Benjamin Silliman, Jr. (1880b) wrote his *Report on the newly discovered auriferous gravels of the Upper Rio Grande del Norte in the Counties of Taos and Rio Arriba, New Mexico.* I have not seen this rather rare 34-page report, but according to F. A. Jones (1904, p. 16), Silliman stated:

> "Here are countless millions of tons of rich gold quartz reduced by the great forces of nature to a condition ready for the hydraulic process, while the entire bed of the Rio Grande for forty miles is a sluice on the bars of which the gold derived from the wearing away of the gravel banks has been accumulating for countless ages, and now lies ready for extraction by the most improved methods of river mining. The thickness of the Rio Grande gravels often exceeds six hundred feet, or three times that of like beds in California, while the average value per cubic yard is believed to be greater than in other accumulations yet discovered."

1881.—Population of Albuquerque: 3,700. The railroad was completed from Albuquerque to Deming, and from the Rio Grande Valley to Gallup and the Arizona line. In a brochure prepared for the Territorial Fair, to be held in Albuquerque Oct. 3–8, it was announced (Anonymous, 1881b) that "We shall show cabinets of minerals from every mining district, most of which will be taken from well developed mines; and bullion from the mills located and in operation." Prizes were announced as follows: $100 for the "best collection of specimen ores from any one mine;" $100 for the "best collection of specimen ores from any one mining district;" and $100 for the "best collection of specimen ores from the Territory at large."

After citing the general abandonment of mining following the Pueblo Revolt in 1680, Howe (1881) wrote:

> "For two hundred years they [the mines] have been lying dormant, but their rest is nearly ended. The tireless prospector will soon cover every hill and mountain. Every stone will be upturned in search of mineral and the wealth of our mountains once more be brought to light."

However, there were marauding Apaches in the Black Range, and in January, "Nana's band of Apaches attacked the camp in Chloride Gulch, killed two prospectors and drove off nearly all the stock."

Anderson and Telegraph districts were prospected. Rich silver ores were found at Black Hawk. Bromide No. 2 district was located. Lead ores were found in the Caballo Mountains. The Chloride district had 200 miners. Council Rock was discovered, and ore was found in the Cuchillo Negro district. Lead-silver ores were found in the Florida Mountains. Hansonburg had 150 men and there were another 100 in surrounding camps. Placer gold was discovered at Hopewell. A group of ten claims at Lake Valley was sold for $450,000. "Prof. B. Silliman has been visiting the Magdalena mine . . . and reports that he is well pleased with what he saw, and thinks that this mining camp is bound to be, at no distant day, of no mean proportions." The first modern prospecting began in the Nacimiento Mountains. In the New Placers district, Golden had 1,000 inhabitants and a newspaper, the *Golden Retort*. According to Howe (1881), pipes were being laid to bring water from reservoirs in the Sandia Mountains to the New Placers, a distance of 15 miles, at a cost of $500,000. Later, excessive pressure caused these pipes to burst on several occasions.

J. P. Whitney purchased the Santa Rita property and erected a stamp mill. A smelter was built at Socorro. In Socorro County, nearly 3,000 locations were made within 6 months. A total of 100 miners were working on Socorro Mountain. The Steeple Rock area was located in January, and the Carlisle mine was reported sold for $250,000. More than 100 locations were made in the Tres Hermanas district, including the "David Crocket." At Ute Creek, 90 nuggets were taken by one man in one year, ranging from $5 to $100 in value, plus 20 ounces of dust. From the old Silver Mountain (Water Canyon) district of Socorro County, one author (Anonymous, 1881c) cited 20 species and several additional varieties of minerals.

A news dispatch from Socorro mentioned the following mining districts:

Alamillo	Chloride Gulch	La Joya
Bear Spring	Cristobal	La Joyita
Black Range	Ladrone	Limitar

Membres	Pueblo	San Zaro
Mogollon	San Mateo	Silver Mountain
Polvadera	San Pedro	

All of these districts were said to be attracting prospectors and visiting capitalists. An intriguing bit of news is the following:

> "Prof. Charles Longuemare, of Socorro, known as "Kernal" in his newspaper contributions to the MINING WORLD, is busy preparing a work on the mineralogy of New Mexico" (*Mining World,* Las Vegas, v. 2, no. 2, Sept. 15, 1881, p. 20).

I have not been able to determine that this "work" was ever published.

1882.—Population of Las Vegas: 7,000; Silver City: 4,000; Georgetown: 1,000. The New Mexico Mining Association was organized at Albuquerque on Sept. 22. Newspapers, mostly weeklies, being published in the Territory included the following: *Miner and Manufacturer* (Albuquerque), *Weekly Chronicle* (Cerrillos), *Silver Brick* (Georgetown), *Golden Retort* (Golden), *Herald* (Lake Valley), *Mining World* (Las Vegas), *Mining News* (Santa Fe), *Mining Chronicle* (Silver City), and both the *Miner* and the *Semi-Weekly Miner* (Socorro).

According to a news item (*Mining World,* Las Vegas, v. 2, no. 14, April 20, 1882, p. 199):

> "This present spring it is safer than it was last year on the eastern slope of the Black Range, for the reason that Gen. MacKenzie runs that part of the Territory. . . . There are four forts in a radius of forty miles. At Silver Camp they have organized a good company among themselves, and have on hand one hundred stands of arms, and also have a good temporary stone fort for their own protection in case of any attack by the Apaches."

Benjamin Silliman, Jr., who had already published several articles on turquois and one on placer gold, gave his observations on the Socorro Peak, Magdalena, Lake Valley, and several other districts, citing a total of 29 minerals. More than 130 mines were reported in the Cerrillos district! The Old Boss mine in the Council Rock district, discovered in April, 1881, was sold for a reported $125,000. Copper properties of the Estey district were sold. Silver was discovered at Fleming. The Mimbres Mining Co. of the Georgetown district produced 170,000 ounces of silver during the past year, employing an average of 250 men. In a letter to the *Mining World* (Anonymous, 1882b, p. 23), D. H. Jackson, superintendent of the Lake Valley mines, wrote:

> "We took out a piece of horn silver today [Aug. 20, 1882]: weight, over 10,000 pounds; worth over $60,000. . . . I took out to-day altogether, with only eight men in eight hours, over one hundred and thirty thousand dollars."

A month later a news item stated that the Lake Valley district was "certainly the richest mining district in the world."

At the San Pedro mine of the New Placers district, "in the palmy days of 1882, 1,000 men were employed in and about this property and the smelter." An assay of 14 tons of ore from the Memphis mine of the Organ district ran $1,554.54 per ton. A single mine in this district was reported sold for $400,000. A total of 500 prospectors were working on the Rio Percha. Gold was found at Rosedale. The Socorro *Miner* announced the "startling discovery" of a "four-foot vein of native copper in the St. Felicite district that is so rich that it will not blast and has to be chiseled." Another news item (*Mining World*, Las Vegas, v. 2, no. 19, July 15, 1882, p. 261) with both poor spelling and poor grammar stated:

> "Considerable quantities of that rare mineral vandamite of lead, a beautiful red chrystal, has been discovered in the St. Felicite district. Any one in search of fine cabinet specimens, will do well to secure some of this vandamite."

The Santa Rita payroll bore 140 names in December. "Silver City has three newspapers, four stamp mills, two smelters; twelve saloons and three churches." There was a big strike in the Telegraph district; horn silver was found in 14 places, with assays running $300 to $500. Native silver was discovered in the Tierra Blanca district. Copper ore was being produced by the quaintly named Hades Cañon Company in the Hell Canyon subdistrict of the Tijeras Canyon district. Two prospectors worked two days on dry placers located 18 miles east of Albuquerque and obtained $504 in gold dust (weighed by a local jeweler). A company was formed to work a group of 14 claims on the Pecos River near Cooper's ranch (later the Willow Creek district).

1883.—For a description of difficulties with marauding Apaches under Victorio, see an article, *The mining regions of southern New Mexico*, by F. M. Endlich (1883). Gold Camp was prospected. At Kingston, streaks of "solid silver sulphide," which assayed 16,530 oz of silver or $18,730.20 were found. A new paper, the *Tribune*, began publication at Kingston. It was reported that 200 men were working at Lake Valley. As many as 200 teams were steadily engaged in hauling ore from the mines at Magdalena to the smelter at Socorro.

About 20 men were working the mica claims of the Nambe district north of Santa Fe. In the New Placers district, the San Pedro mine was producing 40 to 50 tons of ore per day valued at $250 per ton. New Mexico's first mill with a mechanical concentrator was built at Pinos Altos. A group of 20 mines (claims?) in the Potrillo Mountains west of El Paso was sold for $100,000. The Santa Rita mines were now employing 180-200 men. The Steins Pass district was being prospected extensively. In the revised edition of the Dana textbook, E. S. Dana cited 34 species of minerals from New Mexico.

1884.—Las Vegas was now the largest city in either New Mexico or Arizona, with a population of 8,000. Hopes were running high at Lake Valley. About 300 men were at work and in the past three years about $4,000,000 in silver was produced. Bancroft (1888, p. 755) wrote that there was

> ". . . $15,000,000 in sight, ore running $100 to $27,000 per ton. In the 'Bridal Chamber' pure silver may be melted off with a candle; and Gov. Safford offered $50,000 for the ore that he could extract unaided in 10 hours."

Some years later, Gov. Otero (1899, p. 154) reported that a single piece of silver ore removed from the Bridal Chamber was valued at $80,000.

1885.—According to Coan (1925, p. 393), "the earliest list of mining districts accessible is that of 1885." Grant County had 21 districts; Socorro, 13; Sierra, 10; Taos, 6; Lincoln, 6; Bernalillo, 6; San Miguel, 6; Dona Ana, 4; Santa Fe, 2; Valencia, 2; Colfax, 1; and Mora, 1.

Shipments of ore to the Deming smelter were remaining light because of the presence of numerous Indians in the area. Stream tin was discovered in the Taylor Creek district. Alum was shipped from the Hot Springs on the Upper Gila (Alum Mountain district); 12 to 15 mines were reported here. Ores of the Lady Franklin mine of the Kingston district were yielding $14,000 to $20,000 per car. Silver-copper ore of the Coyote Creek district of Mora County was running $300 per ton. The Copper City mines of the Nacimiento Mountains district were now employing 70 men. The town of Kelly in the Magdalena district had a population of 450.

Descloizite, vanadinite, and a new mineral—endlichite—were described from Lake Valley by F. A. Genth and Gerhard vom Rath. H. Baumhauer studied polished sections of copper ore from the Chloride district, using acids as etch reagents to differentiate the various minerals. This was the first application of the microscope to the study of ore minerals!

1888.—According to Howard Bryan, in his column "Off the beaten path" (*Albuquerque Tribune,* Nov. 7, 1955), an article in the *Albuquerque Democrat* of May 18, 1889 stated:

> "Considerable excitement prevails among prospectors regarding the whereabouts of a certain vein of horn silver that is supposed to be hidden by the Indians in the northern portion of the Sandias.
>
> "For years the Pueblos have been known to be the possessors of a secret mine of silver that surpasses in richness anything known to exist in northern New Mexico. They make rings, bracelets and other barbaric ornaments out of pure silver, and when asked where the metal is obtained only answer by a shrug of the shoulders or a grunt."

The article stated further that pieces of the silver ore had been found in arroyos along the western foot of the Sandias, and that an old sheepherder had visited the mine one year before, or in 1888.

1889.—The University of New Mexico at Albuquerque, a school of mines at Socorro, and an agricultural college at Las Cruces were established by the Territorial Legislature. W. F. Hillebrand published a short note on a mineral from the Black Hawk district which later proved to be a new species—nickel-skutterudite. A boom began in the Cochiti district.

1890.—Population of New Mexico: 160,282. According to C. W. Henderson (1933, p. 774), "All authors agree that the hostility of the Apache Indians from 1800 to 1890, when they were subdued, was a serious handicap to mining in the southwestern part of the state."

1891.—The cyanide process was perfected in South Africa, and gold mining was revolutionized. Rich native silver was discovered at the Silver Cell mine in the Pinos Altos district; these ores were refused by the smelters and had to be sent directly to the mint as bullion. Zinc ores at Hanover and iron ores at Fierro were mined in a small way.

1892.—E. S. Dana, in the 6th edition of J. D. Dana's *System of mineralogy,* cited a total of 50 minerals from New Mexico.

1893.—Silver was demonitized; this was followed by a disastrous panic, and prospectors turned from silver back to gold. Black Hawk, Lake Valley, and other silver producers closed down. A minor boom began at Twining, and some prospecting was carried on at Red River.

1896.—Some of the promotional pamphlets and brochures prepared by the Territorial Bureau of Immigration were quite optimistic. For example, one (Anonymous, 1896) bears the title: "The mines of New Mexico; Inexhaustible deposits of gold and silver, copper, lead, iron and coal; A mineral area unequalled in any State or Territory for the extent and value of its mines." A subtitle at the top of the first page reads: "The mines of New Mexico; A mineral belt unequalled on the face of the earth for quality, quantity, or extent; Four hundred miles of gold, silver, copper, lead and coal."

1897.—The Hearst estate took a lease on the Santa Rita property.

1898.—Turquois deposits were developed at Orogrande.

1899.—The Santa Rita property was sold to the Santa Rita Mining Co. According to Gov. Otero's report, this year New Mexico had more than 80 mining districts.

1900.—Population of New Mexico: 195,310. Thomas Edison erected a plant at Dolores to treat the gravels of the Old Placers district; he attempted to extract gold by static electricity. The first important work was done at Picuris; Rociada and Tecolote districts were being developed; some work was being done on the copper deposits of the Burro Mountains. The Estey district was established and about $200,000 was spent on a large electrolytic plant of 100-ton capacity, water line, and various buildings. The value of ore produced to 1904 was only $10,000. As F. A. Jones (1904, p. 105) observed:

> ". . . numerous buildings [were] erected and other magnificent expenditures indulged in; all of this was done before the ore bodies had been properly exploited or a method for the correct and economical treatment of the ores had been investigated."

1901.—The Bureau of Immigration published a 136-page book (Anonymous, 1901a), entitled *Mines and minerals of New Mexico; With some reference to the geological associations in the various camps of the Territory.* In this it is stated that

> ". . . there are 79 official mining districts and 754 patented mining claims in the Territory. . . .
>
> "It should be explained that there are fully 300 organized mining districts and not less than 2,000 mining claims in the territory which are either held unpatented under the federal mining laws or have been purchased or leased from the owners of confirmed land grants" (op. cit., p. 29–30).

In a description of the Ortiz mine of the Old Placers district, it is stated that

> "In 1828, before gold was thought of in connection with California, this mine was making regular shipments of the yellow stuff by mule train to Chihuahua, Mex. In 1833 the Spanish government granted the tract to Ortiz and Cano. A history of the property since would fill a volume of no mean proportions" (op. cit., p. 56).

We read further that in the San Pedro mine of the New Placers district,

> "One can stand erect and walk anywhere in the mine for a distance of five miles, proceeding between walls neatly arched overhead that are literally bespangled with garnet, peacock and azurite gold and copper ores, that weave themselves into beautiful pictures when played upon by the flickering candle light" (op. cit., p. 59).

And, at the Gold Standard mine, 2½ miles southeast of Golden, in the same district,

> "The white quartz is beautifully shot through and through with great chunks of the yellow metal [gold]. Miners at work in the claim say they often pick up nuggets from the floor worth from $2 to $12. Many of these sell at the rate of $40 per ounce, because of their fantastic shapes and their association with pure white quartz crystals, which makes them popular for stickpins and other ornaments" (op. cit., p. 61).

The Bureau of Immigration's report on Bernalillo County (Anonymous, 1901b) is entitled:

"Bernalillo County, New Mexico: The richest and most populous County in the Sunshine Territory; Its resources include agriculture, horticulture, sheep and wool, gold, coal and other minerals; manufactures, railroads, etc."

The most important mining camp in the County was Bland, center of the Cochiti district (now in Sandoval County). The population of Bland and the adjacent camp of Albemarle was 1,200. About 9,000 tons of ore per month was being treated at the Albemarle mill. Other mining camps mentioned as being located in Bernalillo County are Hell Canyon, Coyote Canyon, Las Placitas, San Isidro, Copper City "or Naciemiento," and Algodones.

The El Paso smelter was acquired by the American Smelting and Refining Co., and the plant was enlarged to treat copper and lead ores. This stimulated interest in mining, and many old gold and silver mines were reopened. Sulfur was being produced at the Jemez Sulphur Springs. From 3 to 5 cars of sheet and scrap mica were being shipped each month from Petaca to Chicago and Cleveland. It was estimated that extensive placers on the Rio Chama, 8 miles west of Abiquiu and near the junction of Canones Creek, covered about 1,000 acres and that as much as $10,000,000 in gold might be recovered. It was reported that as a result of 2,665 tests over an area of 16 square miles in the Old Placers district, gold-bearing gravels were found to range up to 65 feet in thickness, and the total gold present was estimated to be $800,000,000!

1902.—Copper ores were being developed in the Burro Mountains district. An important strike of high-grade silver ore was made at Chloride Flat. Phelps, Dodge and Co. purchased the Hanover mine. Jones Camp and the Glenwoody district were established.

1903.—Gold mining in the Cochiti district increased the importance of northern Bernalillo County and resulted in the splitting off of Sandoval County. Douglas Johnson's report on the geology of the Cerrillos Hills was published. Zinc carbonate ores were being developed at Magdalena, and there was important production of these for several years. Keyes (1903b) described the boom in the Pittsburg district of the Caballo Mountains. Over 500 men reached the scene in a single day.

"It would be impossible to describe the wild excitement that prevails at the diggings and at Rincon. Men have apparently gone wild. . . . Everything just now is in the wildest state of confusion. . . ."

1904.—F. A. Jones published his book, *New Mexico mines and minerals,* citing 149 species of minerals. Zinc production began to become important at Magdalena and Hanover. Magdalena became the leading zinc producer of the State and held this rank until 1920. Two smelters were now operating at Silver City.

1905.—The low-grade copper deposits at Santa Rita were examined by

John M. Sully. Phelps, Dodge and Co. purchased the copper property at Leopold in the Burro Mountains district. Zinc ores were produced at Central and Pinos Altos. According to L. C. Graton (1933), in his paper *Life and scientific work of Waldemar Lindgren,* the Division of Mineral Resources of the U. S. Geological Survey was reorganized in 1905, and Lindgren became head of the Section devoted to the precious and semi-precious metals. This same year afforded opportunity to make a comprehensive and systematic study of the ore deposits of an extensive region in relation to the general geology and structure.

> "In what was then the Territory of New Mexico, little geological work had been done by the Federal Government since the early reconnaissances of the Wheeler Survey. Yet mineral deposits were widely spread over the region and, although mining had been going on for more than a century, their importance was plainly increasing. As to the character of these occurrences, little was known; but Lindgren sensed in them the existence of features and relationships of prime importance. The study of the ore deposits of New Mexico was the beginning of similar comprehensive investigations of the mineral resources of the individual states, several of which have already been completed."

The New Mexico report—*The ore deposits of New Mexico*—by Lindgren, Graton, and Gordon, published in 1910, was the first of these reports. The second, on Utah, came ten years later.

1906.—Systematic sampling of the great copper deposit at Santa Rita was begun. This led, in a few years, according to a company brochure, to "open-pit mining of the low-grade ore and development of Chino as one of the nation's major porphyry copper mines, in which mass production is applied to mining ore which may contain well under one percent metallic copper."

1908.—*South-Western Mines,* a monthly mining newspaper edited by F. A. Jones, started publication Oct. 5. The first number carried an article entitled "Mining activity in the Sandias" (Anonymous, 1908c). A review of the Placitas district contains the statement that "the Valley View properties belonging to the well known aeronaut, J. A. Blondin,[11] are showing up quite favorable. . . ." Col. B. Ruppe and associates were

11. I had not a little difficulty determining why Mr. Blondin was reputed to be well known. Eventually I found a news item in the *Albuquerque Journal* (July 7, 1907), reporting that "Joseph A. Blondin, of Albuquerque . . . better known throughout the east as an expert in ballooning and airship trials, proposes to make Albuquerque famous in the world of aeronauts by attempting this fall to beat the record for long distance ballooning held by Lt. Lahm, who won it last year by sailing in a balloon from Paris across the channel to the English coast, a distance of 402 miles."

In 1909, Blondin and Roy A. Stamm became the first in America to make a balloon ascension above 5,000 feet. According to an obituary of Mr. Stamm (*Albuquerque Journal,* Aug. 8, 1957), "The two . . . took off from Sixth and Central, sailed over the Manzano Mountains and reached a height of 13,000 feet before landing two and a half hours later and 90 miles away considerably short of their destination—Kansas. Loss of lift—not bullets which were fired at them by a woodsman near Escabosa—was blamed for the balloon's abrupt descent."

engaged in developing the La Luz mine, near the crest of the Sandias. Also, there was activity in the Carnuel–Tijeras Canyon area, the Hell Canyon "district," and the Coyote Springs "district." In all, a dozen different and independent operations in the Sandia Mountains were described in the article.

The boom at Sylvanite was described in several articles. In one, entitled *New gold camp of Sylvanite* (Anonymous, 1908d), we are informed that the stampede is on and that over 1,000 people are present.

> "Telluride of gold is undoubtedly here . . . Over a score of business houses are now in course of erection. . . . At the beginning of the rush accommodations were, of course, out of the question and considerable suffering from hunger and cold was experienced. . . . A new paper called the Sylvanite Sun has just made its appearance."

Shortly after this a second paper, the *Sylvanite Miner,* made its appearance. According to an article by G. A. Martin (1908):

> "A New Mexico law prevents the opening of a new saloon for a certain period before and after an election and this effectually prevented the sale of liquor in the camp. The owners of the townsite are going to make an effort to keep it out forever and have at least one western mining town without a saloon. Gambling is prohibited entirely by the laws of New Mexico and there is no card playing at Sylvanite.
>
> "Carpenters are getting $25 a day and sign painters get almost any price they ask for painting signs. . . . A doctor and a dentist have set up offices in tents."

Water was packed in on burros and sold for $1 a gallon. The supposed "sylvanite" for which the camp was named was later identified as tetradymite and finally as tellurobismuthite and gold.

1909.—Vanadinite was recognized by J. O. Clifford in the Caballo Mountains. According to an article on the Black Mesa district of Union County (Anonymous, 1909a), the main shaft of the mines of the Fort Pitt Copper Co. was down to 350 feet; from 8 to 16 men were being employed. "It is said that the copper bearing dike can be traced for nearly fifty miles, but only twenty miles of the same at present has shown values of commercial importance."

In an article entitled *Gold near Mountainair* (Anonymous, 1909d), a discovery of gold and copper ore 12 miles east of Mountainair was announced. (This would place it at the north edge of Chupadera Mesa, a few miles south of Willard.) The discovery was made "just below some supposed ancient Spanish workings." Prospectors were flocking in from all directions. "The find consists of particles and wire gold in association with copper ore."

1910.—Population of New Mexico: 327,301. The classic report, *The ore deposits of New Mexico,* by Lindgren, Graton, and Gordon, was published. Large-scale stripping operations by steam shovel were begun at Santa Rita. Zinc production became important at Hanover. All of the following information for 1910 is culled from articles and news items in *South-Western Mines.*

The Octoroon Mining Co. realized $653.39 from a car of 17 tons of lead ore shipped from the Coyote (Tijeras Canyon) district to Joplin, Mo., after deducting the freight and smelting charges. In Sierra County:

> "Considerable prospecting for rare metals such as radium, platinum and its allied metals, as well as for tin, nickel and cobalt is going on in this county where in certain places geological formations favor the occurrence of these minerals and where traces of these minerals have been found."

An article on the Red River district stated that it was the largest district in New Mexico, being 40 miles long and 12 miles wide. "Manozite" (monazite), "uranimite" (uraninite), and other minerals were cited. Great activity was reported from Mogollon, Steeple Rock, Orogrande, Hillsboro, and Magdalena districts. A wild prediction was made that Hell Canyon (Tijeras Canyon) district would rival Bisbee, Arizona! An article on the Headquarters (Hansonburg) district reported lead, silver, high-grade copper, and gold quartz, with 500,000 tons of ore in sight on the surface. "This is what can be truthfully termed a mine on top of the ground." Large shipments of meerschaum were being made regularly from a mine near Silver City. A rich strike was made by Col. John W. Fleming in the Black Hawk district. "The ore is literally full of native silver and runs $5,000 to $7,000 a ton."

1. Top of Old Chalchihuitl Turquois Mine, Cerrillos, New Mexico, c. 1943. Collections in the Museum of New Mexico. Photo by Bill Lippincott.

2. Mine Headframes, Lake Valley, New Mexico, c. 1890-1900. Collections in the Museum of New Mexico. Photo by Henry A. Schmidt.

3. Homestake Shaft, Cerrillos, New Mexico, c. 1881-82. Collections in the Museum of New Mexico. Photo by George C. Bennett.

4. The Grant Tunnel, Cerrillos, New Mexico, c. 1881-82. Collections in the Museum of New Mexico. Photo by George C. Bennett.

5. Prospectors on the Trail, Possibly Near Cerrillos, New Mexico, c. 1881-82. Collections in the Museum of New Mexico. Photo by George C. Bennett.

6. Visiting Dignitaries at Unidentified Mine, Lincoln County, New Mexico, 1904. Collections in the Museum of New Mexico.

7. The Cliff (Later Named King) Mine, Chloride, New Mexico, c. 1886-95. Collections in the Museum of New Mexico. Photo by Henry A. Schmidt.

8. The Good Enough Mine, Apache Mining District, c. 1890. Collections in the Museum of New Mexico.

9. Miners Holding Miners' Candles, Hillsboro or Kingston, New Mexico, c. 1886. Black Range Museum Collection in the Museum of New Mexico. Photo by J. Burge.

10. Placer Gold Dredged at Golden, New Mexico, c. 1915. Collections in the Museum of New Mexico. Photo by T. Harmon Parkhurst.

PART II

Minerals of New Mexico: Descriptions and Records of Occurrence

TURQUOIS—Turquoise

Hydrated basic phosphate of copper and aluminum, $CuAl_6(PO_4)_4(OH)_8 \cdot 4H_2O$. See below.

Triclinic-pinacoidal. Crystals minute and very rare (none found in New Mexico). Usually massive, amorphous or cryptocrystalline. Reniform, stalactitic, incrusting. Often in thin seams or veins, and as disseminated grains. Also as rolled masses and pebbles. Cleavage in crystals only. Fracture small conchoidal to smooth. Rather brittle.

H = 5–6. G = 2.6–2.8. Luster somewhat waxy, feeble (higher in polished material). Color sky-blue, bluish green, apple-green, greenish gray. Some specimens are darker blue in certain kinds of artificial light than in daylight. Color is generally lost on exposure. Streak white or greenish white. Feebly subtranslucent to opaque. Porous, becoming dirty and greasy easily, especially by absorption of oil from the skin. Some specimens fluoresce a mouse-gray color under both short-wave and long-wave ultraviolet light.

A relatively rare mineral in U. S. Various formulas have been proposed: $CuO \cdot 3Al_2O_3 \cdot 2P_2O_5 \cdot 9H_2O$; $H_5(Al[OH]_2)_6Cu(OH)(PO_4)_4$; $Al_2(OH)_3PO_4 \cdot H_2O + x Cu$; $CuAl_6(PO_4)_4(OH)_8 \cdot 5H_2O$; $CuAl_6(PO_4)_4(OH)_2 \cdot 4H_2O$; etc.

For "Bone Turquois" or "Fossil Turquois," see Vivianite var. Odontolite.

Turquois has been mined more or less extensively, but intermittently, in New Mexico for at least twelve hundred years. From several lines of evidence we know that it was held in high esteem by the early inhabitants of the Southwest. Far more turquois has been mined in New Mexico than in any other State. Numerous papers have been written on the mineralogy, geology, mining, utilization, and other aspects of New Mexico turquois. Several analyses have been made; many illustrations, some in color, have been published; and several districts have furnished museum specimens. Because of the unusual interest attached to this mineral, a somewhat longer treatment is accorded it.

The following aspects are here discussed:

Spelling and derivation of name
Bibliography
Records of occurrence

Value of production
Prehistoric mining
Archeology
Mention by early Spanish explorers
The chalchihuitl question
Mythology and folklore
Technology

SPELLING AND DERIVATION OF NAME

The name *turquois* comes from the French, meaning *Turkish stone,* and apparently was applied not because the mineral came from Turkey but because it was introduced into Europe from Persia by way of Turkey.

Certain dictionaries give the preferred spelling as *turquoise,* but James Dwight Dana, in the first edition (1837) of his *System of Mineralogy,* spelled it without the *e,* and most mineralogists have employed the simplified spelling. The word should, perhaps, be pronounced ter-kois′, but it is usually pronounced ter-quoiz′ or tur-koiz′. It may be noted that in modern French, the word is written *turquoise*; in old French, as *tourques*; in Spanish, as *turquesa*; and in German, as *türkis.* The term *chalchihuitl* is discussed later.

BIBLIOGRAPHY

More articles have been published on turquois than on any other New Mexico mineral. The following papers have been devoted, either wholly or in part, to New Mexico turquois. The districts involved are noted for most of these; several papers deal with turquois from two or three districts.

Aitkens (1931)
Anonymous (1879): Cerrillos
Anonymous (1881a): Cerrillos
Anonymous (1881d): Cerrillos
Anonymous (1882a): Cerrillos
Anonymous (1885): Cerrillos
Anonymous (1891a): Burro Mts.
Anonymous (1891b): Burro Mts.
Anonymous (1902b)
Anonymous (1908a): Burro Mts.
Anonymous (1910e): Cerrillos
Ayer (1916): history
Ball (1941): archeology
Bandelier (1892): history
Blake (1858): Cerrillos
Blake (1859a): Cerrillos
Blake (1859b): Cerrillos
Blake (1883): Cerrillos
Blake (1899): archeology
Carnot (1895): Burro Mts.
Clarke (1884): Cerrillos
Clarke (1903): Cerrillos
Clarke (1915): Cerrillos
Clarke and Diller (1886): Cerrillos
Clarke and Diller (1887): Cerrillos
Cowan (1908)
Dana, E. S. (1892)
Dinsmore (1910): Burro Mts.
Farrington (1903)
Fenderson (1897)
Frost and Walter (1906): Cerrillos
Genth (1890): Cerrillos
Hammond and Rey (1940): history
Harrington (1939b)

Harrington (1940a)
Herrick (1900a): Cerrillos
Hidden (1893): Orogrande and Burro Mts.
Hyde, D. C. (not dated): Cerrillos
Johnson, D. W. (1903): Cerrillos
Jones, F. A. (1904)
Jones, F. A. (1908a)
Jones, F. A. (1909a)
Jones, F. A. (1909d): archeology
Jones, F. A. (1915)
Judd (1925): archeology
Jung (1932): Cerrillos
Knaus (1948): Burro Mts.
Kunz (1885)
Kunz (1890)
Kunz (1893a)
Kunz (1893b)
Kunz (1904): Cerrillos
Lakes (1901): Cerrillos
Lasky (1947): Eureka
Le Conte (1868): Cerrillos
Lindgren, Graton, and Gordon (1910)
Loew (1875b): Cerrillos
Manly (1950)
Newberry (1861): Cerrillos
Newberry (1876): Cerrillos
Otero (1899): Cerrillos
Otero (1900): Cerrillos
Otero (1901): Cerrillos
Otero (1902): Cerrillos
Otero (1903): Burro Mts.
Paige (1912): Burro Mts.
Penfield (1900)
Pepper (1905): archeology
Pepper (1909): archeology
Petersen (1898): Burro Mts.
Pogue (1915)
Pough (1954)
Raunheim (1891): Cerrillos
Reid (1903): Burro Mts.
Reiter, W. S. (1933): archeology
Roberts (1929): archeology
Rösler (1902): Cerrillos
Scholes (1935): history
Schrader, Stone, and Sanford (1917)
Silliman (1880a): Cerrillos
Silliman (1880c): Cerrillos
Silliman (1881): Cerrillos
Smith, R. V. (1908)
Snow (1891): Burro Mts.
Sterrett (1908a): Burro Mts.
Sterrett (1909): Eureka
Sterrett (1911): Burro Mts. and Eureka
Sterrett (1912): Cerrillos
Sterrett (1913b): Burro Mts.
Sterrett (1916): White Signal
Stevenson, J. J. (1881): Cerrillos
Talmage and Wootton (1937)
Thornton (1893)
Wuestner (1932): Santa Rita
Zalinski (1907): Burro Mts.
Zalinski (1908): Burro Mts.

Pogue's (1915) monograph, entitled *The turquois: A study of its history, mineralogy, geology, ethnology, archaeology, mythology, folklore, and technology,* is a work of great interest. This quarto volume, of 162 pages and 23 plates, including two in color, contains numerous references to New Mexico. Its bibliography gives 435 titles, many of which are not included in the U. S. Geol. Survey *Bibliography.* Many ethnologic and archeologic papers treating of New Mexico turquois are cited by Pogue; most of these are not repeated here.

RECORDS OF OCCURRENCE

Dona Ana.—Organ district: at the Torpedo mine, locally a small quantity replacing kaolinite.

Grant.—Burro Mountains, Eureka, Santa Rita, and White Signal districts. Burro Mountains district: *numerous descriptions, several illustrations (some in color), analyses, museum specimens, prehistoric workings, considerable production.* There are numerous mines and prospects at several localities in this district. The most notable mine is the Azure, about 10 miles southwest of Silver City and 1½ miles north of Leopold. Turquois occurs as veins and nuggets; the veins range from 1/16 to 1½ in. thick, usually from ⅛ to ⅜ in. thick; the nuggets are of various shapes—reniform, botryoidal, etc. (Zalinski, 1907). According to Kunz (1893a, p. 545), the turquois "traverses the rocks in seams and streaks, one mass of which measured eight inches in diameter and was one-eighth to one-fourth of an inch in thickness."

Sterrett (1908a, p. 829–830) observed that

> "nearly all shades of blue and green occur—dark blue, sky blue, light blue, bluish green, light green, and dark green—and in some cases reddish-brown, chocolate, and violet-colored material has practically the same composition as turquoise. . . . The turquoise from the Elizabeth pocket [at the Azure mine] is probably the finest ever found in the world. Much of it is of a deep blue color, slightly translucent, and over 6 in hardness, so that it makes a fine wearing gem."

Turquois in the Burro Mountains district was discovered by John E. Coleman in 1875. The Azure Mining Co. was organized in 1891 and two years later the Elizabeth pocket was discovered. In 1900, in the Azure pit a shaft 40 feet deep was found; this was obviously a prehistoric shaft (Knaus, 1948). It has been stated (Anonymous, 1908a) that the Azure mine was the largest open cut in the world made in the mining of turquois. It has been claimed that the Elizabeth pocket, opened in 1893, produced more high-grade turquois than any single deposit on record. In 1908 a nugget of pure turquois weighing 1,500 carats was found. Analysis 1 by A. Carnot (1895; repeated by Zalinski, 1907, p. 483; Jones, F. A., 1909d; and Pogue, 1915, p. 26). Analysis 2 by Theodor Petersen (1898; repeated by Pogue, 1915, p. 26).

	1	*2*	
P_2O_5	28.29	27.09	
Al_2O_3	34.32	32.14	
H_2O	18.24	19.58	
CuO	7.41	4.92	
Fe_2O_3	——	1.33	
FeO	0.91	——	
CaO	7.93	5.23	
MgO	trace	0.89	(incl. Na_2O and K_2O)
MnO	trace	——	
F	trace	——	
Quartz or clay	2.73	8.71	(SiO_2)
	99.83	99.89	

Burro Mountains turquois was described at length by Petersen (1898), in an article entitled *Zur Kenntniss der natürlichen Phosphate; 1. Türkis aus Neu-Mexiko*, excerpts from which are given below*:

"Next to Persian turquois, the best known is the so-called Egyptian from the Valley of Megara near Sinai, which was exploited by the ancient Egyptians. Egyptian turquois is frequently green and fades more readily and more quickly than does the Persian. The occurrences at Jordansmühl in Silesia and Oelsnitz in Saxony are inconsiderable, while on the other hand those in New Mexico aroused the attention of the ancient Mexicans, who prized beautiful turquois more highly than gold. The recently revived mines lie in the Hills of Los Cerillos [Cerrillos], south of Santa Fe, and in the vicinity of eruptive trachytes, which likewise bear copper ores and are generally decomposed and appear bleached by volcanic vapors.

"In such an almost white, obviously bleached and decomposed porphyritic rock in the Borron [sic] Mountains of New Mexico, which was submitted to me in several little pieces . . . are found little veinlets of turquois.

"This turquois is beautiful sky-blue in portions, particularly in thin seams, also somewhat greenish, amorphous, its fracture small conchoidal to uneven, the streak bluish white. . . . The hardness is 6. The specific gravity, based on a number of polished pieces of this turquois, ranging from 0.3 to 0.6 gram in weight, employing two different accurate pycnometers at 15° C, was determined to range from 2.733 to 2.741 (average: 2.737). . . ."

Petersen gives the analysis (see analysis 2 above) and discusses the composition; he concludes that the formula is $2Al_2O_3 \cdot P_2O_5 \cdot 5H_2O$.

Eureka district: *descriptions, illustrations (some in color), prehistoric workings*. There are numerous mines and prospects in the vicinity of Old Hachita and Turquoise Mountain, 6 miles west of Hachita. These mines and prospects were described in some detail by Sterrett (1911). Lasky (1947, p. 81) wrote:

"The Eureka district was many years ago one of the four major turquoise-producing districts in New Mexico, whose stones have been noted for their quality. The Eureka deposits, which appear to have been worked long before the coming of white men to New Mexico, were rediscovered about 1885 and operated intermittently for about 25 years."

Lasky (op. cit., p. 81–82) quoted at length from Sterrett (1911) and added:

"Characteristically the turquoise is in veins or rock that contained considerable pyrite, the oxidation of which produced much clay and jarosite in the rock, which is Sterrett's 'decomposed trachyte.' . . . A thin

* I am indebted to D. A. McKenzie for assistance with the translation.

section of one specimen discloses that the turquoise is veined and replaced by jarosite and by clay minerals. . . . The origin of the turquoise perhaps is, as described by Sidney Paige (1912) for the deposits of the Burro Mountains, that the phosphate of the turquoise was derived from the original apatite by sulfate solutions produced through oxidation of the pyrite."

Santa Rita district: a single specimen of turquois was cited by Wuestner (1932). White Signal district: at several localities.

Hidalgo.—Red Hill district: according to Sterrett (1911), "Turquoise is reported to have been worked several years ago by Nick Rascom at Silver Night, about 20 miles to the southwest of the present mines [of the Eureka district]." Lasky (1947, p. 81) noted in a footnote that "this would place the Silver Night workings in the Animas Range, across Playas Valley." Former citations of prehistoric workings for turquois in the Sylvanite district are apparently erroneous.

Lincoln.—Nogal district: a small quantity has been reported.

Otero.—Orogrande district: *museum specimens, prehistoric workings.* There are several mines and prospects and abundant evidence of prehistoric mining.

Rio Arriba.—A large quantity of turquois was reported to have been found about 4 miles south of the town of Gallina (*Albuquerque Journal*, June 8, 1936). Its occurrence here is quite unlikely and the report should certainly be discounted.

Santa Fe.—Cerrillos district: *many descriptions, numerous illustrations (some in color), analyses, museum specimens, prehistoric workings.* According to Pogue (1915, p. 52), this district contains "the most important deposits of turquois in the United States, from the point of view of their history and past production." What appears to be the first technical paper devoted to any New Mexico mineral was one on the turquois of this district by W. P. Blake in 1858. The first analysis of Cerrillos turquois was made by Oscar Loew in 1875. The eminent Benjamin Silliman, Jr. visited the district in 1880. According to D. C. Hyde (undated brochure), in development work starting about 1880, a number of sealed-up caves were found. In these old workings, small veins of turquois from 1/8 to 2 in. thick were found, along with gold-bearing quartz on the walls of the central cave.

During the summer of 1885 a large suite of specimens was collected by Major J. W. Powell; these were studied by F. W. Clarke and J. S. Diller, who published descriptions and analyses in 1886 and 1887. Kunz (1890, p. 54–59) and many others have described the mines of this district. Douglas W. Johnson (1903) described the geology and petrology at length. The prehistoric workings are described below in a separate section. Modern mining operations have been carried on at several localities, notably at Turquois Hill, 5½–6 miles east of north of Cerrillos (including the Tiffany and Castilian mines), and on Mount Chalchihuitl, about 2½ miles north of Cerrillos. There are also several deposits of lesser importance.

The turquois occurs imbedded in its matrix as nodules but more often as seams or veins. Its color varies widely, ranging from a pure sky-blue through many shades of bluish green and apple-green to dark green showing no blue whatever. Dark green nodules often shade off to nearly white at the center, sometimes resembling certain varieties of malachite. Many specimens are seamed or streaked with limonite; pyrite is occasionally found bright and unaltered, completely inclosed in clear blue turquois. For the green turquois, G = 2.426–2.651 (Blake); for the pale blue turquois, G = 2.805 (Clarke and Diller); for turquois of unspecified color, G = 2.697–2.764 (Jung).

Analyses 1, 2, and 3 by F. W. Clarke (in Clarke and Diller, 1886, p. 212; 1887, p. 40; repeated by Kunz, 1890, p. 58 and 64; Dana, 1892, p. 844; Clarke, 1903, p. 98; Johnson, D. W., 1903, p. 202; Jones, F. A., 1904, p. 271; Zalinski, 1907, p. 483; Anonymous, 1908a; Jones, 1908a; 1909d; Clarke, 1915, p. 351; Jones, 1915, p. 53; Pogue, 1915, p. 26). Specimen 1 = bright blue; 2 = pale blue and slightly greenish; 3 = dark green. Analysis 4 by Oscar Loew (1875b, p. 1027; repeated by J. J. Stevenson, 1881, p. 405; Johnson, 1903, p. 202; Zalinski, 1907, p. 483 [several errors here]; Pogue, 1915, p. 26). Analysis 5 by H. Jung (1932).

	1	*2*	*3*	*4*	*5*
P_2O_5	31.96	32.86	28.63	29.57	34.41
H_2O	19.80	19.60	18.49	18.85	19.35
Al_2O_3	39.53 (with Fe_2O_3)	36.88	37.88	29.17	33.42
Fe_2O_3		2.40	4.07	....	4.37
FeO	....	....	....	4.35	0.72
CuO	6.30	7.51	6.56	4.04	7.70
CaO	0.13	0.38	....	1.61	....
SiO_2	1.15	0.16	4.20	12.57	*
	98.87	99.79	99.83	100.16	99.97

* Recalculated after deducting 2.24 percent SiO_2.

An abstract by L. J. Spencer of Jung's (1932) paper, *Über Türkis,* gives analysis 5 for a specimen from "Los Cerillos," and adds: "agreeing with W. T. Schaller's formula $(Cu,Fe)O \cdot 3(Al,Fe)_2O_3 \cdot 2P_2O_5 \cdot 9H_2O$. Previous analyses tabulated and plotted show considerable variation, as is to be expected with a mineral that was deposited in a colloidal form."

Manly (1950, fig. 2, no. 3) gives a differential thermal curve for a specimen of turquois from an undesignated New Mexico locality, noting the composition $2Al_2O_3 \cdot P_2O_5 \cdot 5H_2O$. For illustrations in color, see Kunz (1890), Pough (1954, pl. 17), and others.

Sierra.—Erroneous citation: prehistoric workings and some modern mining were reported (Anonymous, 1891a; Pogue, 1915, p. 58) "near Paschal," said to be located in Sierra County. The assignment of Paschal to Sierra County was an error, for it is located in the Burro Mountains of Grant County (Otero, 1899, p. 318; Frost, 1890, p. 171).

VALUE OF PRODUCTION

In addition to the large quantities of turquois mined in prehistoric time and during the Spanish period, for which not even estimates are available, much has been mined during the past century. No accurate records of production exist, but some of the estimates are given here.

Governor Thornton (1893, p. 13) wrote that "there are single gems from Santa Fe County now in New York held as high [as] $4,000, and some in Santa Fe of nearly equal size and quality."

A few years later, Governor Otero (1899, p. 159) gave the following figures for value of New Mexico turquois, presumably all from the Cerrillos district, "as taken from official sources":

1891	$150,000
1892	175,000
1893	200,000
1894	250,000
1895	350,000
1896	475,000
1891–1896	$1,600,000

Otero added: "but it is openly asserted that the true value of turquoise mined since 1890 has been greatly underestimated. . . . One single stone taken out is reported to have been bought for $6,000 in New York."

In another connection, Otero (1899, p. 153) wrote that the output of the Cerrillos mine alone, "since 1890, according to official report, has been about $2,000,000, although the former owner of the property claims this to be an underestimate, and says the yearly output since 1893 will reach $1,500,000." Note that the latter estimate would give a total of $9,000,000 for the period 1894–99. See also Otero (1900). According to Pogue (1915, p. 52),

> "New Mexico has produced a greater quantity of turquois than any other State. . . . Its total production probably exceeds $5,000,000 in value.
>
> "The total yield from the holdings of the American Turquois Co., coming chiefly from the 'Tiffany mine,' [in the Cerrillos district] is said to exceed $2,000,000 in value. . . . [This mine is reported] to have produced a higher proportion of high-grade gem material than any other deposit in the United States; its choicest stones have been equalled in this country only by those from the Burro Mountains and some localities in Nevada."

The Azure mine, in the Burro Mountains district, "has been operated in modern times more extensively than any other turquois mine in this country, and its stones are the equal of the Persian gems. The total value of its output is stated to have been between $2,000,000 and $4,000,000."

Note that if we accept $2,000,000 as the figure for Cerrillos production and $4,000,000 as the figure for Burro Mountains production, the total for these two districts alone would be $6,000,000. It is entirely possible that the figure for Cerrillos may be on the order of $9,000,000 and that for Burro Mountains on the order of $5,000,000, so that the total for these two districts may run to $14,000,000. As Talmage and Wootton (1937, p. 89) have well said: "There are many conflicting statements on turquoise production in the various statistical publications and in the literature of New Mexico turquoise."

PREHISTORIC MINING

It has been stated that "There seems to be but little doubt that the mining of turquoise antedates any other kind of mining conducted in the United States" (Anonymous, 1908a). F. A. Jones (1909d, p. 1) observed "that no turquoise deposits of any note have ever been found in the west that did not show the evidence of prehistoric mining."

Mount Chalchihuitl, in the Cerrillos district of Santa Fe County, appears to be "the site of the most extensive prehistoric mining operations known on the American continent," according to Pogue (1915, p. 52). Douglas Johnson (1903, p. 88) declared that "the extent of the workings in Mt. Chalchihuitl is truly marvelous. It seems almost incredible that such a mass of rock could have been removed by a primitive people, without the aid of modern mining appliances." Blake (1858; quoted by Pogue, 1915, p. 52) wrote that he

> "was struck with astonishment at the extent of the excavations. . . . It appears to be 200 feet in depth and 300 or more in width. . . . at the bottom pine trees over a hundred years old are now growing. This great excavation is made in the solid rock, and tens of thousands of tons of rock have been broken out."

Silliman (1881) stated that he was "deeply impressed with the enormous amount of labor which in ancient times has been expended here. The waste or debris excavated in the former workings covers an area which the local surveyor assured me extends by his measurement over at least 20 acres."

On the other hand, in 1911 Sterrett (1912, p. 1067) made measurements of this main pit and found it to be

> ". . . about 130 feet deep on the upper side and about 35 feet deep on the lower side, the rim about 200 feet across, and the bottom nearly 100 feet across. The large dumps of waste rock removed from this are about 150 yards long by 75 yards wide and 1 to 30 feet deep. These dimensions do not correspond closely with those given by the earlier

> writers, since this would give the dump an area of less than 2½ acres as compared with some 20 acres reported by Silliman."

Numerous prehistoric workings have been found at several other localities in the Cerrillos district, some underground as well as at the surface. Many stone hammers and other primitive implements have been found. F. A. Jones (1904, p. 269) observed:

> "The writer with his own hands took from the old excavation at Mount Chalchihuitl, two stone hammers, which are here reproduced [fig. 43].
>
> "It is said that a stone hammer weighing some twenty pounds, with a portion of the handle still intact about the groove, was taken from these same excavations a few years ago. These stone hammers are made from a hornblende-andesite, common to the Cerrillos hills.
>
> "Similar implements and tools of stone have been taken out of the old mines and dumps, in the Burro mountains, Hachita [Eureka district] and in the Jarillas [Orogrande district]."

ARCHEOLOGY

We know that turquois mining began more than twelve centuries ago, for Roberts (1929) found pendants of turquois at Shabik'eshchee, a late Basket Maker site in Chaco Canyon. This village was built and inhabited toward the end of Basket Maker III, perhaps a century or more prior to A. D. 777.

The abundance of turquois recovered by archeologists from Pueblo Bonito, in Chaco Canyon, is truly astounding. In the years 1897–99 the Hyde Expedition collected more than 50,000 pieces of turquois; this material dates back to the period A.D. 950–1150. A number of inlaid items were described and illustrated in color by Pepper (1905); these include a bone scraper inlaid with "jet" and turquois, a "jet" frog with turquois eyes, and a buckle or breast ornament of "jet" inlaid with turquois; also a number of beads, pendants, and carved birds—all of turquois.

In another paper, Pepper (1909) described the contents of a small burial room about 6 ft square, which, among many other items, included the amazing total of 24,932 turquois beads and more than 700 turquois pendants. One skeleton, for example, had associated with it a total of 5,891 beads and several pendants of turquois, the largest pendant being 45 mm long. A still more gorgeously arrayed skeleton had 8,385 beads and more than 500 pendants; these had originally been worn as wristlets, anklets, and ornaments over the breast and abdomen; on the left wrist alone were found 2,388 beads and 194 small pendants. Near these skeletons was a remarkable cylindrical basket 6 in. high and 3 in. in diameter, onto which had been cemented a mosaic of 1,214 pieces of turquois. Inside the basket were found 2,150 beads, 152 small pendants, and 22 large pendants, the largest of which measured 36 by 27 by 3 mm. Pepper concluded that Cerrillos was the chief source of this turquois, that the burials represented persons of considerable rank, and that at this time the Chaco people were at the height of their esthetic arts.

Judd (1925) also found at Pueblo Bonito a string of 2,500 turquois beads which he described and illustrated in color. Winifred Reiter (1933) described pendants found at Chetro Ketl, another ruin in Chaco Canyon; her thesis on the jewelry and ornaments of the ancient Pueblo Indians includes many references to turquois.

Several workers have concluded that turquois was an important item of trade in prehistoric times. Ball (1941, p. 17, 25) states that "New Mexican turquoise reached Mexico City and the Mayan cities," and that the early trade in Southwestern turquois extended "from the West Indies and Yucatan on the south to Ontario on the north . . . and from California on the west to Mississippi and Arkansas on the east." He notes that Earl Morris found a mosaic plaque set with 3,000 pieces of turquois at Chichen Itza, Yucatan, and concludes that this turquois "doubtless, was largely of New Mexican origin."

In this connection, Pogue (1915, p. 104) remarks:

> "No occurrence at all adequate as an important source has been discovered south of the present Mexican boundary. It therefore seems probable that the Aztecs and allied peoples, through trade with tribes to the north, obtained supplies of turquois from the Cerrillos hills and perhaps other localities of the Southwest."

Several writers have referred to "Aztec" mines and "Aztec" mining operations in New Mexico. Sterrett (1911), for example, wrote:

> "the first work done on the turquoise deposits of [the Eureka district] was by Con Ryan and [Sterling Burwell] between 1885 and 1888. This work was done for gold, as Con Ryan supposed that the ancient workings and dumps in the region were gold mines of the Aztecs or early Spaniards."

In citing world localities for turquois, Ramdohr (1948, p. 518) mentions "Los Cerillos (Mt. Chalchuitl) in New Mexico, where it was mined by the Aztecs long ago." It is almost certain that Aztecs did not venture this far north to engage in mining operations.

MENTION BY EARLY SPANISH EXPLORERS

From the reports of the early Spanish explorers, it would appear that the Indians of New Mexico, Arizona, and northern Mexico had an abundance of turquois in the form of beads, pendants, and various inlaid ornaments. The mineral also was employed in the decoration of houses, both on interior walls and on exteriors, such as doorways. Furthermore, the mineral served as an item of trade. Several significant references to turquois are here given in chronological order.

1539.—On his journey northward through Mexico and Arizona toward Cibola (Zuni, New Mexico), Fray Marcos de Niza visited pueblo after pueblo, the inhabitants of which possessed great quantities of turquois jewelry, notably strings of beads and nose and ear pendants. On several occasions he heard that at Cibola the portals and doorways were decorated with the mineral. In his report of 1539, Fray Marcos mentioned turquois no less than fourteen times (translation by Hammond and Rey, 1940, p. 66–79). Estéban, the Negro, who had been sent on ahead to explore, must have collected some turquois en route, for Castañeda stated that when "Estéban reached Cibola, he arrived there laden with a large number of turquoises and with some pretty women, which the natives had given him" (translation by Hammond and Rey, 1940, p. 198).

1540.—In his letter to the King, Viceroy Mendoza quoted Capt. Melchior Díaz as saying, in his letter of March 20, that the Indians at Cibola "have turquoises in quantity" (Hammond and Rey, 1940, p. 159). In his letter of August 3 to the Viceroy, Coronado mentioned turquois given him by the Indians at Cibola, some of which he said he was sending to Mendoza (op. cit., p. 176–177). Turquois is mentioned several times in Castañeda's history of the Coronado expedition; a significant record is that the Indians at Cicuye (Pecos) presented Capt. Alvarado and his soldiers with quantities of turquoises, "which are found in abundance in that region" (op. cit., p. 219).

1629.—Fray Gerónimo de Zárate Salmerón, in his *Relaciones,* mentioned "minas de Chalchihuites" or deposits of turquois, "which the Indians have worked since heathen times, since to them it is as diamonds and precious stones" (original Spanish in Bandelier, 1892, p. 94; translation by Eleanor B. Adams).

1630.—Fray Alonso de Benavides, in his *Memorial,* observed that the Indians "deck themselves out . . . with necklaces and earrings of turquoises, for they have mines of these, and cut them, though imperfectly" (translation by Ayer, 1916, p. 34).

Up to 1680.—During the period prior to 1680, turquois was "a standard article of inter-pueblo trade," according to Scholes (1935, p. 96). A news dispatch from Turquesa, Santa Fe County (Anonymous, 1881d), stated:

> "We have the evidence that the Spaniards have worked a great many mines in this [Cerrillos] district. Only a few of them have been reopened, and in every instance we have found rich deposits of ore. The old Turquoise mine has furnished most of the turquoise used in the world."

F. A. Jones (1909d) stated that

> ". . . while tradition from the early Spanish records tends to convey the idea that these mines were worked by the Jesuit Fathers prior to the year 1680, there has never been, to the writer's knowledge, a single cop-

per or iron utensil or anything of distinctly Spanish origin that would tend to prove any of this work was done under Spanish rule."

Jones (1904, p. 273) wrote:

> "In the elaborate ancient ramifications of the old workings at Mount Chalchihuitl, which were extensively prospected a few years ago, many stone hammers, whole vessels of ancient pottery and various crude mining implements were found. It is said that some twenty Indians were killed, about 1680, by the caving of a large portion of the works; this was claimed to be one of the chief causes which led to the general uprising of the Pueblos, that shortly afterward drove the Spaniards from the country."

According to another account (Anonymous, 1885), in 1680 the whole top of the mountain caved in, burying about 80 Indian miners.

THE CHALCHIHUITL QUESTION

Pogue (1915, p. 105–109) devotes a chapter of his monograph to the problem of chalchihuitl. In ancient Spanish writings there are numerous references to a green stone highly prized by the Aztecs of Mexico and called by them *chalchihuitl*. Many workers have speculated as to the mineralogical identity of this material. Blake, in several of his papers, argued that the green turquois of New Mexico should be called chalchihuitl. Apparently, in Mexico much of this material may have been jade; in New Mexico much of it was green (but not blue) turquois. In a recent paper entitled *Chalchihuitl—A study in jade,* Foshag (1955) does not even mention turquois. He states that all Meso-American jade proves to be jadeite and that most of it may have come from a deposit in Guatemala.

It may be noted further that the word has been spelled in various ways, such as:

Calchihuite	Chalchiuitl
Calchivites	Chalchuhuites
Chalchigüite	Chalchuite
Chalchihuis	Chalchuitl
Chalchihuite	Chalchuitt
Chalchihuitl	Chalcibetes
Chalchilhuith	Charchihuites
Chalchithuils	Thalchuitl

MYTHOLOGY AND FOLKLORE

There are many references to turquois in the literature of mythology and folklore.* Pogue (1915, p. 110) notes that

* Mythology has been defined as the superstitions of the ignorant of the past; folklore as the superstitions of the ignorant of today.

"turquois is peculiarly rich in its list of reputed achievements and in this respect is exceeded by few gems. Its early use, its ready fashioning by primitive people unskilled in the art of working the harder stones, and its occurrence within reach of diverse and widely separated races; its range of color, suggesting both the blue of sky and the green of water and of verdure, and its tendency to alter in shade, bespeaking a power within itself—all these have connected the turquois with many superstitions not only of the Ancients but of the ignorant of today. . . . From remote ages blue has been a significant color and its emblematic use widespread."

Merrill (1922, p. 177) observed that turquois is

"highly valued by all orientals and worn by them to insure health and success. Supposed to preserve the wearer from injury through accidents. . . . Its color paled as its owner sickened and was lost entirely on his death. . . . According to Arabian and Persian authorities [it] cured all diseases of the head and heart. A sovereign remedy for hernia, swellings, flatulence, dyspepsia, insanity, and cancerous sores. Whether taken alone, mixed with honey or with other drugs, it cures epilepsy, spleen, and stricture. In cases of poisoning or snake bite it was given with wine. . . . Applied as an ointment to the eyes it increased their luster, restored the vision. . . . Worn as an amulet the turquoise brought happiness, dispelled fear, and rendered its wearer safe from drowning, lightning stroke, and snake bite. In Egypt cure of a cataract is believed to be effected by the local application of a turquoise set in a silver ring and dipped in water."

There is apparently no generally accepted list of birthstones. Merrill (1922, p. 152) cited turquois as the birthstone for December, but Pogue (1915, p. 118) stated that Kunz cited it as the birthstone for July, and that Tiffany and Co. once cited it for both June and July.

TECHNOLOGY

Mining.—It is a curious fact that turquois is usually found only in arid or desert regions and that it always occurs at shallow depths, practically never in any quantity below 100 ft. The mineral is usually mined in open cuts, such as trenches or pits. After crushing, the material must be sorted by hand. A difficulty in prospecting for turquois is that it weathers easily upon exposure, loses its color, and eventually crumbles to a powder. Nodules with a white exterior, however, may have an unaltered core of good material. F. A. Jones (1909d) wrote that the ore is

"taken from the mine to a specially arranged sorting room having a ceiling of white cheese-cloth and white window shades, where the rock fragments are dumped on tables covered with oil cloth. The work of sorting is done under the watchful eye of the superintendent, in order that no valuable stones may be appropriated by the workingmen. . . ."

Cutting.—Turquois is never faceted as are such stones as the diamond, sapphire, ruby, emerald, and other transparent gems. It is usually cut in the form of a *cabochon*, with a flat base and a convex top. With this form, of course, numerous variations are possible; the shape may be circular, oval, square, etc.; the convexity of the arch may vary considerably. After cutting, the upper surface is polished.

A finished stone may be composed of pure turquois or of turquois and country rock or vein material, such as yellow, brown, or reddish limonite, jarosite, quartz, and other minerals. This associated foreign matter is termed *matrix*, and a stone containing considerable matrix is termed *turquois matrix*. *Rock turquois* is a term that has been applied to a matrix of turquois in which small grains of turquois are imbedded. In cutting, advantage may be taken of attractive patterns and contrasts furnished by the irregular distribution of matrix, and the value of the stone may be enhanced by its presence.

Alteration of color.—That some turquois was subject to fading was well known to the ancients. As a matter of fact, this tendency led to many superstitions in the early days and the investing of the mineral with supernatural power. For centuries, apparently, there was rather general belief that the color of the stone depended on the health of its owner. It was further believed by some that turquois lost its color if worn by lewd or immodest persons and that the fidelity of a lover could be tested by this means.

The fact that the color could be deepened or improved artificially was discovered at an early date. In the 13th century a Persian writer observed that the color could be altered by the application of butter or mutton fat. It is said that the natives near the great mines of Nishapur, in Persia, often carry stones in their mouths before offering them for sale. Blake (1883, p. 199) noted that the Indians of the Southwest soaked their turquois in tallow or grease. Inferior stones may be stained with Prussian blue (Kunz, 1890, p. 58–59), and a patent was once granted on a process which involved immersion in baths of various chemicals to give a permanent blue color.

Precautions.—The relative softness of the mineral necessitates not a little care in wearing. The polished surface is easily marred and roughened by contact with harder materials. It has been stated that, in order to avoid loss of color, turquois should never be permitted to absorb perspiration, skin oils, or perfumes, and that turquois rings should be removed before washing the hands so as to avoid contact with soapy and greasy water.

Imitations.—Turquois has been extensively imitated for many centuries in various countries. The three general types of imitations are 1) glass or enamel (these usually have a vitreous or glassy luster); 2) synthetic compounds (difficult to distinguish; sometimes even matrix is faked); and 3) substitutes. The latter include such minerals as odontolite or "bone turquois" (vivianite), lazulite, lapis lazuli, chrysocolla, chalcedony, azurite, malachite, variscite, and others. Sometimes the color of these substitutes is artificially altered.

An interesting record of deception at an early date in the American period is by Lieut. J. G. Bourke, who, in his diary (Bloom, 1936, p. 78), noted on April 22, 1881, that

> "A number of the young men from San Domingo boarded our train to sell specimens of what they called 'chalchuitl' (turquoise) of which I purchased three pieces. It is not genuine turquoise, but rather an impure malachite. . . . The real turquoise, however, is found in New Mexico and is held at an extravagant valuation by *all* the Indians of the South-West."

This expanded section on turquois may be appropriately concluded with the following news item (Anonymous, 1910e), which will serve to indicate just how extravagant the valuation was:

> *"Tiffany turquoise mines robbed by Santa Domingo Indians*
>
> "Threatening him with death if he interfered with their plans of robbing the Tiffany turquoise mines, 14 miles south of Santa Fe, N. M., a band of Santa Domingo Indians approached the home of Manager J. P. McNulty and after leaving a guard of about 16 warriors at the mouth of the shaft, descended the 125-foot shaft by means of a rope, ascending with some of the much sought for stone. Efforts have been made by Santa Fe officials to capture some of the band. . . .
>
> "The Indians still claim the turquoise mines from which their forefathers took turquoise centuries ago, but the title is in the American Turquoise Company [in] which the Tiffanys of New York are the principle [sic] stockholders."

VIVIANITE—Odontolite

Octahydrated iron phosphate, $Fe_3(PO_4)_2 \cdot 8H_2O$.

Monoclinic. Crystals prismatic. Also reniform, globular, incrusting, fibrous, or earthy. Cleavage highly perfect in one direction. Fracture fibrous. Flexible in thin laminae. Sectile.

H = 1½–2. G = 2.6–2.7. Luster pearly to vitreous, dull. Colorless, blue, green; may deepen on exposure. Streak white to bluish white, changing to blue or brown. Transparent to translucent to opaque.

ODONTOLITE (Bone Turquois, Fossil Turquois, etc.) includes fossil teeth, ivory, bones, shells, roots, etc. colored blue or green by vivianite. Pogue (1915, p. 132) remarks: "This material, which was often confused in the Middle Ages with true turquois, is fossil bone or ivory impregnated by phosphate of iron, and possesses a blue color scarcely distinguishable in some instances from that of mineral turquois in daylight, but appearing a dull-gray by artificial illumination. (Much bone turquois is greenish in color and does not greatly resemble mineral turquois.)"

According to Dana (1892, p. 845), "Much of the turquois (not artificial) used in jewelry in former centuries, as well as the present, and that described in the early works on minerals, was *bone-turquois* (called also *odontolite* . . .), which is fossil-bone, or tooth, colored by a phosphate of iron."

ODONTOLITE

Sandoval.—Nacimiento Mountains district: in describing the copper deposits of the Nacimiento Mountains, F. A. Jones (1904, p. 188) writes:

> "The copper appears to have come from the saliferous beds of the Permian; since it occurs in the [Triassic] conglomerates and sandstones which immediately overlie that series. Precipitation of the cupric solutions seems to have been due to the presence of carbonaceous matter, rather than to the association of iron. In evidence of this may be seen the impress of leaves, reeds and portions of trees which have been completely transformed into some forms of copper ore, preserving permanently their original outlines. Some teeth of extinct saurians have been taken out of these beds, which are classed as odontolite, by reason of their cupriferous impregnations."

SILVER

Native silver, Ag.

Isometric. Crystals commonly small, distorted, in acicular forms and reticulated or arborescent shapes. Often as coarse to fine wires; also massive, in scales and plates, or in grains. Cleavage none. Fracture hackly. Ductile and malleable. H = 2½–3. G = 10.1–11.1; 10.5 when pure. Luster metallic. Color and streak silver-white; often gray-yellow, or brown to black, by tarnish. Opaque.

AMALGAM (Mercurian Silver) contains mercury.

AURIAN SILVER contains gold; color often brass-yellow.

PLATANKA is a term that was widely used by prospectors and miners in New Mexico in the early days. It apparently represents a corruption of the Spanish term, *plata blanca,* for native silver.

SILVER

Bernalillo.—Tijeras Canyon district: in the early days there were frequent reports of a small quantity of silver in the Hell Canyon district; this may have referred to argentiferous galena.

Catron.—Mogollon district: rather rare, as minute plates and wire.

Colfax.—Baldy district.

Dona Ana.—Organ district: at several mines. Argentiferous galena collected in 1864 by Owen and Cox (1865, p. 17–18, 55–56) at the San Adelia mine and also at the Stevenson (or Stephenson) silver mine. The silver-lead was cupelled by Cox and gave 1.80 percent silver, stated to represent 204.80 oz per ton or "256 dollars standard coin." Wire silver was found at the Little Buck mine, as noted in the following news item (*Mining World*, Las Vegas, v. 2, no. 21, Aug. 15, 1882, p. 292):

> "The wonderful strike of native or wire silver and horn silver (chloride) in the Little Buck mine continues to create the greatest excitement . . . some pieces of ore . . . the size of two fists . . . with wire silver from the size of matches down running all through the ore."

The Galloway mine yielded much native silver (Dunham, 1935).

Grant.—Black Hawk, Burro Mountains, Central, Chloride Flat, Eureka, Fleming, Georgetown, Gold Hill, Lone Mountain, Pinos Altos, Santa Rita, and White Signal districts. Black Hawk district: *several descriptions*; according to a news item in 1883, the ore body of the Black Hawk mine at Bullard's Peak was 14 in. wide at the surface and almost solid native silver; at a depth of 20–25 ft, the ore changed to argentite or ruby silver. Another account (*Mining World*, Las Vegas, v. 5, no. 4, Dec., 1885, p. 57) stated that a car of ore shipped from the Rose mine "was a satin spar [probably a carbonate such as ankerite or siderite] carrying native silver and crystallized argentite in enormous quantities. Chunks of from twenty to thirty pounds in weight . . . from half to three-quarters silver." A rich strike by Col. J. W. Fleming on the Chicago claim was reported in Dec., 1910: "the ore is literally full of native silver and runs $5,000 to $7,000 a ton." According to A. A. Leach (1916) ore from the Alhambra mine carried 300 to 2,000 oz of silver per ton; at the Black Hawk mine, "The native silver . . . was very massive and was mined literally in sheets weighing up to 200 lb. Specimens of the ore resemble globs of melted coin." It was reported that the owners had much difficulty with high-graders. "Much of the ore was massive native silver which, it is stated, averaged the high-graders from $800 to $1,000 a sack."

In a description of nickel ore of the Alhambra mine, Hess (1917b, p. 753) wrote:

> "In a letter dated October 21, 1916, W. George Waring states that in 1893 and 1894:
>
> 'At the time of my visit there was one solid mass of native silver 60 or 70 feet long, 6 inches to 18 inches thick, extending 1 or 2 feet above the floor of the drift for the entire length of the mass. The arsenical nickel mineral or minerals [nickel-skutterudite] did not accompany this mass—they were found farther southwest, near to the Rose mine, in which they were fairly abundant.'
>
> "In one place in the Alhambra vein a shoot, possibly the one just referred to in the quotation from Waring, from 2 to 3 feet wide . . . is said to have carried from 15 to 20 per cent of nickel, in the form of niccolite. . . ."

Krieger (1935, illus.) observed silver in arborescent masses, with good crystalline form, associated with nickel-skutterudite. Massive silver from the Black Hawk mine is radioactive, according to Gillerman and Whitebread (1956).

Burro Mountains district: traces of silver in the Shrine fluorspar vein. Chloride Flat district: in plates as large as a silver dollar (Entwistle, 1944a). Eureka district: wire silver occurred at the American and King mines (Lasky, 1947); also, at the Hornet mine (R. A. Zeller, Jr., memo., Nov. 22, 1955). Lone Mountain district: as curved bundles of wire (Paige, 1916). Pinos Altos district: wire silver was found in vugs, breccias, and chimneys; "huge lumps are usual" and "slabs of almost pure metal varying in width from a half-centimeter to 6 centimeters are sometimes found," according to Blood (1916). Santa Rita district: in traces, as thin films (Wuestner, 1932). White Signal district: in a quartz vein at the Moneymaker fluorspar deposit (Gillerman, 1952a). Also, east of the White Signal district, at the Malpai Tanks fluorspar deposit: an old silver mine (ibid.).

Hidalgo.—Lordsburg, San Simon, and Sylvanite districts. Lordsburg district: locally, as "large patches and wires." Sylvanite district: in the Jowell vein.

Lincoln.—Estey district: wire silver was reported in "an old shaft worked hundreds of years ago" somewhere in the Oscura Mountains, 50 miles southeast of Socorro (*Mining World*, Las Vegas, v. 1, no. 6, Feb., 1881, p. 12).

Luna.—Carrizalillo (?), Tres Hermanas, and Victorio districts. Tres Hermanas district: at both the Hancock and Hercules mines. Victorio district: in 1882 a news item reported "platanka silver" at the Victoria (sic) mine.

Rio Arriba.—Ojo Caliente No. 1 district: a very small quantity reported.

Sandoval.—Placitas district: in 1909, Emil Kleinwort struck "some very high grade silver ore. One nugget, as large as an egg, of almost pure silver was taken out" (*South-Western Mines*, v. 1, no. 12, Sept. 5, 1909, p. 5).

San Miguel.—Tecolote district: wire silver was found at Mineral Hill in 1881.

Santa Fe.—Cerrillos and New Placers districts. Cerrillos district: native silver was observed in the Bonanza No. 1 mine and wire silver elsewhere in the district (Anonymous, 1881e). In 1882 wire silver was reported from a mine near "Mina de Tiera." New Placers district: "very fine free gold and silver" were seen at San Pedro in 1883 by Carl Henrich (1887); according to Dale Carlson (memo., Oct. 5, 1953), a small amount of silver was found at the Carnahan mine, as wires associated with pyrolusite, cerussite, anglesite, and papierspath calcite.

Sierra.—Chloride, Hermosa, Hillsboro, Kingston, Lake Valley, and Tierra Blanca districts. Hermosa district: formerly fairly common, but now rather rare (Jicha, 1954a). Kingston district: abundant; wire silver cited in news items in 1883. Tierra Blanca district: a news item (April, 1882) reported that native silver had been discovered in the "Bromide" district, at "Sierra [sic] Blanca."

Socorro.—Cat Mountain, Ladron, Magdalena, North Magdalena, San Jose, Socorro Peak, and Water Canyon districts. Magdalena district: silver was found as thin plates in allophane and chrysocolla; at the Anchor mine, wire silver in seams and crevices; at the Black Cloud mine, as specks. North Magdalena district: formerly common as needles.

Taos.—Red River district: rare; fine wire silver is said to have been found at the Black Rock group or old Buffalo property.

Union.—Folsom district (?): reported from northeast of Folsom.

Valencia.—Zuni Mountains district: probably minor.

AMALGAM

Socorro.—Ladron district: unverified occurrence. According to Leeson (1896, p. 44), both "amalgam" and "silver-amalgam" occur in this district. I know of no recent confirmation of this reported occurrence. See also the discussion under Cinnabar of the Spanish term *azogue.*

Silver Blende. See Argentite.
Silver Carbonate. No such mineral is known to exist. The term, as used by early miners, apparently referred to silver-bearing cerussite.
Silver Chloride. See Cerargyrite.
Silver Glance. See Argentite.

Silver Minerals

Undetermined silver minerals have been cited from several localities.

Bernalillo.—Placitas and Tijeras Canyon districts. Tijeras Canyon district: in the Carnuel and Coyote Springs subdistricts (Anonymous, 1908c).

Dona Ana.—Potrillo Mountains district.

Grant.—Central district: Ground Hog mine. According to Lasky (1935c), no definite silver minerals can be recognized, but the average ore contains 10 oz of silver per ton. Lasky believes that the silver mineral or minerals are not contained in chalcopyrite or sphalerite but are submicroscopic in size and located in the black chalcocitic tarnish on chalcopyrite and sphalerite.

Lincoln.—Jicarilla district.

Mora.—At several places: Apache Hill; Mora region; near Ocate; Turkey Mountains (Anonymous, 1880a). In 1885, silver was reported in the copper ore of the Coyote Creek district.

Sandoval.—Placitas district.

San Miguel.—Tecolote district. Near Hot Springs, 6 miles northwest of Las Vegas (Anonymous, 1880a).

Sierra.—Caballo Mountains, Fra Cristobal, Hermosa, and Lava Gap districts. Caballo Mountains district: silver ore reported at the Homestake mine of Humboldt camp in 1882. Fra Cristobal district: at the Jim Blaine mine, silver was reported in 1882. Hermosa district: an undetermined mineral, apparently a double sulfide of silver and lead, reported by Jicha (1954). Lava Gap district: silver ore reported in 1910 from the old Red Canyon district.

Socorro.—Council Rock and Mockingbird Gap districts. Council Rock district: in 1882 silver was reported found in the slag of ancient Spanish smelters. Mockingbird Gap district: reported in 1910.

Torrance - Socorro - Valencia.—Southwest slope of the Manzano Mountains, sometimes referred to in early reports as Spiegelburg camp: the ruins of twenty-two apparently ancient Spanish smelters were reported in 1880, with native silver present in the slag (Anonymous, 1880b). According to D'Oro (1881), some of the ore contained 22 oz of silver per ton.

GOLD

Native gold, Au.

Isometric. Distinct crystals rare, commonly distorted. Usually filiform, reticulated, dendritic; massive; in thin laminae; often as flattened grains or scales. Cleavage none. Fracture hackly. Very malleable and ductile. H = 2½–3. G = 15.6–19.3. Luster metallic. Color and streak gold-yellow, sometimes inclining to silver-white, and rarely to orange-red; often brass-yellow to pale yellow. Does not tarnish. Opaque.

ARGENTIAN GOLD: silver is usually alloyed with gold in varying amounts, such as 0–15 percent. The color becomes paler with increase in silver.

ELECTRUM is a term applied when the silver content exceeds 20 percent.

Gold is commonly reported as 1) lode deposits, and 2) placer deposits. See E. H. Wells and T. P. Wootton (1932) and Wootton (1940).

LODE DEPOSITS (Most of these carry native gold)

Bernalillo.—Placitas and Tijeras Canyon districts: rare. A news story in 1882 reported that gold "in considerable quantities" had been found in slag near ancient smelters "at many places in the Sandia Mountains."

Catron.—Mogollon and Wilcox districts.

Colfax.—Baldy, Cimarroncito, and Elizabethtown districts. Baldy district: as wire and thread gold, and as coarse leaf gold in thin irregularly shaped masses; usually as minute particles coated with some dark material (Raymond, 1870; Lee, 1916). According to Brevoort (1874, p. 80), the Commissioner of the General Land Office reported he had received a specimen of ore from the Aztec mine, "through which are interspersed fibers of pure gold, some of which exceed two in. in length."

De Baca.—At the pyrolusite deposit on the S. A. Steele ranch, Coyote

Creek, about 6 miles west of Fort Sumner, a dollar's worth of gold was obtained from 20 lbs of "dirt" from the prospect shaft (Allen, K., 1939).

Dona Ana.—Bear Canyon, Black Mountain, Gold Camp, Organ, Potrillo Mountains, San Andres Canyon, and Texas districts. Black Mountain district: according to a news item (*Mining World,* Las Vegas, v. 3, no. 7, Jan. 1, 1883, p. 108), the Mountain Chief and Copper Duke mines are showing "the largest mass of nuggets, flour and scale gold ever seen. One lump weighed 3 pounds was four-fifths pure gold." Organ district: "fine specimens of free gold" were reported in 1882; later, gold flecks were observed in acicular malachite.

Eddy.—Early reports of gold in the Guadalupe Mountains.

Grant.—Bound Ranch, Burro Mountains, Carpenter, Central, Fierro-Hanover, Gold Hill, Malone, Pinos Altos, Ricolite, Santa Rita, Silver City, Steeple Rock, Telegraph, and White Signal districts. Fierro-Hanover district: as wires in sphalerite. Ricolite district: the New Mexico Ricolite Company reported finding high-grade gold ore (Anonymous, 1946a). Silver City district: in assays. Steeple Rock district: free gold left after oxidation of pyrite; "many beautiful gold specimens are taken out" (Pickard, 1912).

Harding.—Gold-quartz stringers have been noted north and west of Bueyeros.

Hidalgo.—Apache No. 2, Fremont, Lordsburg, Red Hill, Steins Pass, and Sylvanite districts. Sylvanite district: the most important constituent of the veins; as rough grains, clusters, or threads, invariably associated with tetradymite.

Lincoln.—Estey, Gallinas Mountains, Jicarilla, Nogal, and White Oaks districts. Estey district: wire gold reported in "an old shaft worked hundreds of years ago" somewhere in the Sierra Oscura, 50 miles southeast of Socorro (*Mining World,* Las Vegas, v. 1, no. 6, Feb., 1881, p. 12). According to Peters (1882), the copper ores of the Estey district contain gold. Jicarilla district: according to Walter A. Hubbard (letters, Jan. 9 and March 10, 1943), analyses of ores by Frank P. Baldi revealed at least three types: 1) the simple gold-silver selenide, 2) a very complex gold selenide tied into a sulfo-arsenide, and 3) another very complex gold selenide and antimonide; see further under "Gold Selenide." White Oaks district: a gold nugget about the size of a pullet egg was found in the Homestake mine; it was worth $182.50 (*Mining World,* Las Vegas, v. 1, no. 8, April, 1881, p. 13). Beautiful specimens of wire gold were found in the Little Mac mine in June, 1881. It was reported in March, 1882 that a chunk of gold about the size and shape of a large Bartlett pear, weighing 2 lbs and 7 oz and worth $542.50, had come from the Little Mac. At the South Homestake mine, "every shot brings to light gold flecked quartz . . . lumps of rock as large as a man's head with bunches of wire gold and frosted with flower gold" (*Mining World,* Las Vegas, v. 2, no. 17, June 15, 1882, p. 241). According to E. P. Smith and L. Dominian (1904),

"An interesting, and probably unique, instance of the occurrence of native gold in gypsum is found in the Old Abe mine. The hydrous calcium sulphate occurs at the contact of the shales and the augite porphyrite. . . . A specimen showed fine wires of gold in a slab of gypsum."

F. A. Jones (1904, p. 173) also commented on this unique occurrence of "virgin gold in gypsum," but Lindgren, Graton, and Gordon (1910, p. 180) observed that the supposed gypsum proved to be a "soft, bleached, chalky phase of the much-altered monzonite."

Luna.—Carrizalillo, Tres Hermanas, and Victorio districts.

Mora.—Wire gold was reported in 1882 from a locality 7 miles from Mora. Later, it was said to occur on the north fork of Rio de la Casa, 9 miles west of Mora. Reported also from northeast of Chacon. According to Anderson (1956, p. 142), "several small, very rich pockets of gold ore have been found in the lenses of quartz in the Precambrian rocks near the upper reaches of [Rio de la Casa]."

Otero.—Guadalupe Mountains, Orogrande, and Tularosa districts. Guadalupe Mountains district: reported but needs verification.

Rio Arriba.—Bromide No. 2, El Rito, Hopewell, and Ojo Caliente No. 1 districts. El Rito district: in a conglomerate. Ojo Caliente No. 1 district: only a small quantity reported.

Sandoval.—Cochiti, Jemez Springs, and Placitas districts. Placitas district: reported from both the La Madera and Sandia subdistricts.

San Miguel.—Rociada, Tecolote, and Willow Creek districts. Tecolote district: at Mineral Hill. Also at a group of claims 10 miles south of Bernal (Chapelle).

Santa Fe.—Cerrillos, Glorieta, New Placers, Old Placers, and Santa Fe districts. Cerrillos district: about 1880, gold-bearing quartz was found by D. C. Hyde (undated brochure) on the walls of a sealed-up cave. One writer (Anonymous, 1881d) refers to "gold in quartz"; another (Anonymous, 1881e) noted wire gold. News items mention wire gold at several places in 1882. Glorieta district: in the old Bradley mine and at the Jones claims. New Placers district: very fine specimens of leaf and wire gold, some inclosed in translucent to transparent calcite. According to Statz (1909a), the gold is dark colored, "being coated by a rusty or yellowish brown film." A few years later, Statz (1912a) observed that the gold is associated with lenses of magnetite and quartz, and that

"A characteristic of the gold found in these pockets is that it is often very coarse and is inclined to be smooth, round and flattened in shape. Both fine flakes and solid nuggets are quite common. . . . [In a] somewhat intermediate type of pocket . . . gold is associated with quartz lenses in veins. This gold is also commonly quite coarse, and is characterized by rough, ragged edges, peculiarities which are distinguishable in the nuggets found in the placer mines of the camp."

Old Placers district: formerly much wire gold; in 1864, Prof. Richard E. Owen and E. T. Cox took more than 100 lbs of gold-quartz ore from the Ortiz shaft; assay by Cox (in Owen and Cox, 1865, p. 15; repeated p. 49):

Gold	Silver	Iridium	Total
99.170	0.782	0.048	100.00

Sierra.—Caballo Mountains, Chloride, Goodfortune Creek, Hermosa, Hillsboro, Iron Mountain No. 2, Kingston (rare), San Mateo Mountains, and Tierra Blanca districts. Chloride district: "very rich silver ore fairly spangled with free gold" was found at the Ivanhoe mine in 1882. Goodfortune Creek district: gold is said to have been mined here in 1655 and from then until 1712; later the deposit was rediscovered by Dr. C. F. Blackington, who named it the Good Fortune (Leeson, 1896, p. 43). Hillsboro district: in the Bonanza mine, pyrite crystals were bound together by heavy wires of gold (Harley, 1934).

Socorro.—Cat Mountain, Council Rock, Hansonburg, Lemitar Mountains, Magdalena, Mill Canyon, Mockingbird Gap, North Magdalena, Ojo Caliente No. 2, Rosedale, San Jose, San Lorenzo, Socorro Peak, and Water Canyon districts. Council Rock district: the slag of ancient Spanish smelters yielded gold in 1882. Lemitar Mountains district: a news item (July 15, 1882) states: "The recent rich finds of gold in the Polvadaro [Polvadera or Lemitar Mountains] and St. Felicite [Santa Felicita; location problematical, possibly the Socorro Peak] districts, are attracting much attention." Magdalena district: uncommon; as grains and wires with cerussite and willemite at the Stonewall mine (Lasky and Loughlin, 1943, p. 99); wire gold in seams in limestone reported by Tom Tarr (1938). Mill Canyon district: rare. Mockingbird Gap district: gold values reported in lead and copper ores in 1910. Water Canyon district: rare.

Taos.—Anchor, Glenwoody, Picuris, Red River, Rio Grande Valley, and Twining districts.

Torrance.—"Particles and wire gold in association with copper ores" reported from the old Spiegelburg Camp area, but also located specifically 12 miles east of Mountainair, which would place it at the north edge of Chupadera Mesa, a few miles south of Willard (Anonymous, 1909d).

Union.—Folsom district.

Valencia.—Zuni Mountains district: a small quantity reported.

PLACER DEPOSITS

Bernalillo.—Tijeras Canyon district: placer nuggets up to $40 each reported by Burke (1896, p. 24) from the Hell Canyon subdistrict.

Chaves.—Along the Rio Hondo. Also, very low gold values reported from weathered rock of the Railroad Mountain dike, northeast of Acme.

Colfax.—Baldy, Cimarroncito, Elizabethtown, and Ponil districts.

Grant.—Gold Hill, Malone, Pinos Altos, and Steeple Rock districts. Steeple Rock district: placer gold in Apache Creek (Pickard, 1912).

Harding.—In the valley of Ute Creek, near Gallegos.

Hidalgo.—Lordsburg and Sylvanite districts. Sylvanite district: placer deposits worked; nuggets as much as one ounce (Lasky, 1947).

Lincoln.—Gallinas Mountains, Jicarilla, Nogal, and White Oaks districts. Also along the Rio Hondo.

Mora.—At a locality 1 mile southwest of Mora.

Otero.—Orogrande district.

Quay.—Reported in the early days along Revuelito Creek, 18 miles east of Tucumcari, in grains are large as wheat; according to F. A. Jones (1904, p. 19), the ground had been salted.

Rio Arriba.—Abiquiu and Hopewell districts.

Sandoval.—Placitas district.

San Miguel.—Willow Creek district.

Santa Fe.—Cerrillos, New Placers, Old Placers, and Santa Fe districts; also along Galisteo Creek. The Old and New Placers districts have yielded nearly $4,000,000 or about 25 percent of the total placer yield of New Mexico (Wootton, 1940, p. 16). The Old Placers were discovered in 1828, and the New Placers in 1839. They have been visited and described by several explorers and geologists. Placer gold from the New Placers was analyzed by Dr. F. A. Wislizenus in 1846 (Wislizenus, 1848, p. 32; repeated by Blake, 1856a, p. 94; by J. J. Stevenson, 1881, p. 399):

Gold	Silver	Iron and Silica	Total
92.5	3.5	4.0	100.00

According to a news item in 1882, a 7-lb nugget was found in 1843. According to Dale Carlson (memo., Oct. 5, 1953), some coarse nuggets in the New Placers district have cavities lined with wires and crystals.

Sierra.—Hillsboro, Las Animas Placer, and Pittsburg districts.

Taos.—Anchor, Glenwoody, Red River, Rio Colorado Placers, Rio Grande Valley, and Twining districts.

Union.—Folsom district.

"Gold Chloride." No such mineral is known.

Taos.—Red River district: "chlorides of gold and silver" were reported by R. P. Kelly (1909).

Gold Dust. Fine particles of gold such as are obtained from placer deposits. Compare dust gold, float gold, and flour gold.

Gold Selenide.

Lincoln.—Jicarilla district: according to Walter A. Hubbard (letters, Jan. 9 and March 10, 1943), ores collected by him were submitted in 1938 to Dr. E. E. Bagbee, of Massachusetts Institute of Technology, who reported that some of the material was "similar to the rare gold selenide described by Lindgren in the Republic district, Washington." See Lindgren and Bancroft (1914, p. 148–150) for a discussion of a suspected gold selenide, possibly Au_2Se_3, in the Republic district of Washington.

OUTSTANDING MINERALS

Actinolite.—Rocks composed largely of actinolite were used extensively by prehistoric Indians for axes and hammers.

Alabandite.—Common in Kingston district.

Altaite.—Not uncommon locally in the Organ district.

Alunogen.—Extensive deposit in Alum Mountain district.

Ammonia alum.—Somewhere near Tucumcari.

Andalusite.—Striking groups of crystals in Hondo Canyon district.

Anglesite.—Good specimens in several districts, especially Hansonburg.

Anhydrite.—Great thicknesses in subsurface of southeastern New Mexico.

Aphthitalite.—First record for U. S.: Carlsbad Potash district.

Aragonite.—First record for the world of floating films: Carlsbad Caverns. "Mirage stones" used in Navajo ceremonials. Striking crystals: Magdalena district. Triplets: Chaves, De Baca, Guadalupe, and Quay Counties. Material with showy fire-red fluorescence: Lincoln and Lea Counties. Flos-ferri: Organ district.

Argentite.—Widespread and locally abundant.

Arsenopyrite.—Twins and triplets in Tres Hermanas district.

Atomsite.—Glass produced by fusion of soil of the Jornada del Muerto during the world's first atomic explosion.

Augite.—An occurrence near Cabezon Peak was the subject of a master's thesis. Segregations several inches in diameter: Kilbourne Hole.

Aurichalcite.—Showy specimens in Magdalena district. Mineral proved to be optically negative.

Autunite.—Excellent material in several districts.

Azurite.—Crystals at numerous localities; those from Magdalena were unusually rich in forms and intensely brilliant. Georgetown district: pseudomorphs of copper, malachite, and clay—all after azurite.

Barite.—Widespread and locally abundant. Spectacular sheaves in Tijeras Canyon district. Good material in Hansonburg, Magdalena, Sulphur Canyon, and other districts. Currently being deposited by modern springs at Ojo Caliente.

Bastnaesite.—Gallinas Mountains district.

Beryl.—Widespread in the Petaca district; crystals up to 8 ft long. Cesian beryl abundant at Harding mine.

Bismuth.—Small quantities in several districts.

Bismuthinite.—In small quantities, as good specimens.

Bismutite.—Widespread in the Petaca pegmatites, in which large masses have occasionally been found. Good material at other localities.

Bixbyite.—Taylor Creek district; second record for the U. S. and third for the world; two new forms.

Bloedite.—Abundant locally in Estancia Salt district; some crystals of large size found.

Bornite.—Widespread and locally abundant.

Bournonite.—Good specimens from Central and Cerrillos districts.

Bromyrite.—In several districts.

Brucite.—Abundant, and in large masses, as brucite marble: South Canyon district.

Calcite.—Iceland spar: a quantity of optical-grade spar shipped from the second and third largest crystals of calcite in the world; some of the material is strikingly banded in pink: Harding Mine district. New crystal forms: Hillsboro district. Octahedron-like crystals and many others: Magdalena district. Manganoan calcite is widespread. Fluorescent uranoan calcite: Tres Hermanas district. Radioactive tufa and travertine in several counties. Oolites and pisolites: first discovery of pisolites in a cave at Carlsbad Caverns. First discovery in North America of pisolites in a spring deposit at Soda Dam, near Jemez Springs. Pisolites are currently forming in a mineral spring near Suwanee.

Caledonite.—Proved to be orthorhombic on a crystal from the Organ district.

Carnallite.—Abundant in Carlsbad Potash district.

Carnotite.—Widespread, especially in McKinley County.

Cassiterite.—A small quantity mined in Taylor Creek district.

Cerargyrite.—Abundant in several districts. Formerly so massive at Lake Valley that it was sawed from the stope! Embolite: excellent material at Georgetown; formerly mined as ore at Lake Valley.

Cerussite.—Large twin crystals from Organ district. Also abundant in several other districts, notably Central and Magdalena.

Chalcanthite.—Good specimens in several districts.

Chalcocite.—Widespread and abundant; pseudomorphs after other minerals in several districts. Notable replacements of fossil wood in many red-beds copper deposits.

Chalcophanite.—Formerly not uncommon as specimens of museum quality: Magdalena district.

Chalcopyrite.—Widespread and locally abundant. Large crystals: New Placers district.

Chrysocolla.—Common in several districts.

Clinozoisite.—Notable occurrence in Iron Mountain No. 2 district.

Coffinite.—This new mineral, described in 1955, is locally not uncommon in McKinley and Valencia Counties.

Columbite.—Large crystals and large aggregates; also as remakable feathery aggregates: Petaca district. Shipments have been made from several districts.

Colusite.—La Bajada district.

Copper.—Showy specimens abundant, especially in several districts of Grant County; excellent crystals at Santa Rita. As sheets, plates, leaves, arborescent growths, pseudomorphs, etc.

Covellite.—Locally common, in several districts.

Cristobalite.—At several localities.

Cryptomelane.—*Type material for this new species,* described in 1942, came from New Mexico, Arizona, and India.

Cubanite.—First record for U. S.: Fierro-Hanover district.

Cuprite.—Beautiful crystals from several districts, notably Fierro-Hanover, Santa Rita, and Magdalena.

Cyanotrichite.—Showy but rare: Hansonburg district.

Descloizite.—Georgetown district: exceptional crystals with extremely brilliant coloring. Lake Valley district: most perfect and best developed crystals known (at least up to 1885). Cuprodescloizite: conspicuous in small quantities.

Diopside.—South Canyon district: crystals rich in forms. Large nodules in Mitten Rock, San Juan County. Malacolite: of light blue color, on Gila River. Salite: bladed crystals up to 6 in. long, common in Fierro-Hanover district.

Dolomite.—Octahedron-like crystals: near Lake Arthur. Pseudomorphs after triplets of aragonite: near Dunlap.

Dumortierite.—Notable specimens: Petaca and Tres Hermanas districts.

Dunhamite.—*Type locality for this new species,* described in 1946: Organ district.

Endlichite.—*Type locality for this new species* (or variety): Lake Valley district; beautiful crystals.

Epidote.—Abundant and widespread.

Eudialyte.—Third record for U. S.: Cornudas Mountains.

Euxenite.—Elk Mountain district; age—1,030 million years.

Fergusonite.—Petaca district; age—150 million years.

Ferrimolybdite.—Conspicuous in Red River district.

Fluorite.—New Mexico has a heavier concentration of fluorite deposits than any other western State. Notable crystals are abundant in many districts. Fluorite is currently being deposited by hot-spring waters at Ojo Caliente. The temperature of crystallization of a crystal from Fluorite Ridge district was determined. Dark purple to black fluorite is always radioactive.

Galena.—Good crystals abundant and widespread.

Garnet.—Garnets of several subspecies are widespread and locally abundant. Pyrope: gem material, unequalled elsewhere in the world, occurs in the Buell Park–Red Lake area, along the Arizona–New Mexico line;

readily collected from ant hills. Spessartite: large aggregates are locally abundant in the Petaca pegmatites.

Glauberite.—New crystal forms: Carlsbad Potash district.

Gold.—Widespread and locally abundant as both lode and placer deposits.

Greenockite.—Small but conspicuous masses in Fierro-Hanover district.

Gypsum.—Great abundance in the State; rock gypsum has been exploited to some extent in more than half the counties. The most notable accumulation of gypsum dune sand in the world: White Sands. West of the White Sands is an abundance of giant crystals. Thin plates of selenite from several localities were used for windows in the early days. Notable crystals in certain caves.

Halite.—A tremendous tonnage in the Permian Basin of southeastern New Mexico. In the Carlsbad Potash district, some halite has patches of intense blue color; much halite is intergrown with sylvite as halosylvite or sylvinite. Salt has been harvested for centuries from the salt lakes of the Estancia and Quemado districts.

Halotrichite.—Abundant in the Alum Mountain district.

Hedenbergite.—The variety mangan-hedenbergite is abundant in the Fierro-Hanover district.

Helvite.—Largest deposits known in U. S. were discovered in 1941: Iron Mountain No. 2 district.

Hematite.—Abundant and widespread. Excellent crystals from Catron County, Santa Fe County, and elsewhere. Numerous notable occurrences of pseudomorphs, oolitic iron ore, etc.

Hemimorphite.—New crystal form: Organ district.

Hessite.—Formerly the principal ore at a mine in Tierra Blanca district.

Hydromagnesite.—As "moon milk," in Carlsbad Caverns.

Iddingsite.—Excellent material in the Brazos River area.

Idocrase.—Beryllium-bearing idocrase: Iron Mountain No. 2 district.

Ilmenite.—Locally not uncommon in the Petaca district.

Iodyrite.—Notable crystals in Lake Valley district.

Iron.—Of the 31 or more meteorites recorded for New Mexico, 14 are nickel-irons. The largest weighed 1,060 pounds.

Jarosite.—Northern Franklin Mountains district: a remarkable deposit of very pure material.

Johannsenite.—*One of several type localities for this new species,* described in 1937: Fierro-Hanover district.

Kainite.—First record for U. S.: Carlsbad Potash district.

Kieserite.—First record for U. S.: Carlsbad Potash district.

Kyanite.—Petaca district: excellent specimens; some mined.

Langbeinite.—First record for U. S.: Carlsbad Potash district. A considerable tonnage has been mined by one company.

Leonite.—First record for U. S.: Carlsbad Potash district. Mineral proved to be optically positive.

Lepidolite.—A large tonnage mined at the Harding mine. Several age determinations have been made.

Linarite.—Showy material of intense blue color at Hansonburg.

Lueneburgite.—First record for U. S. and second for the world: Carlsbad Potash district.

Magnesite.—Abundant in South Canyon district, Dona Ana County, and on Ash Creek, Grant County.

Magnetite.—Age of magnetite in Fierro-Hanover district—53 million years.

Malachite.—Beautiful specimens at many localities. Notable association with fossil wood in several red-beds copper deposits.

Manganite.—Good crystals in several districts.

Martite.—Reported to have been common at Fierro.

Melanotekite.—Hillsboro district: excellent material, affording a new formula; apparently the first record for U. S. and the second for the world.

Meta-autunite.—Much autunite alters to meta-autunite on drying.

Metatorbernite.—In several districts. Probably more abundant than torbernite.

Metatyuyamunite.—Widespread in the Grants and Laguna districts.

Microcline.—Giant crystals, weighing many tons: Petaca district. Showy specimens of pink to lilac and purple color: Harding mine.

Microlite.—Possibly the largest body of microlite in the world: Harding mine; striking crystals in purple muscovite.

Minium.—Caballo Mountains district: good specimens.

Molybdenite.—Red River district: a unique high-grade deposit; up to 1934, this was the second largest producer in the world.

Monazite.—Petaca district: good specimens; crystals, feathery aggregates, large masses. Age—858-886 million years; some calculations—1,330-1,730 million years.

Montmorillonite.—Widespread; deposits in many counties.

Murdochite.—Interesting occurrence of this new mineral: Hansonburg district.

Muscovite.—Extensively mined for many years in the Petaca district. Showy specimens of pink, rose, lilac, lavender, violet, and purple color: Harding mine.

Natrojarosite.—Cooks Peak district.

Nickel-skutterudite.—*Type locality for this new species:* Black Hawk district.

Niter.—Abundant and widespread, especially in Hidalgo County; also in Socorro County.

Novacekite.—First record for North America and second for the world: Grants district.

Olivine.—Excellent gem peridots, said to be the finest in the world, occur in McKinley County, in the Buell Park–Red Lake area, along the Arizona–New Mexico line. Excellent gems, sometimes claimed to be superior to any other, occur at Kilbourne Hole, in Dona Ana County; granular segregations here range up to 18 in. in diameter. A notable occurrence of gem peridots in the Glorieta meteorite—a rare example of "celestial" rather than terrestrial gems.

Opal.—Opalized wood and uranoan opal in several localities.

Orthoclase.—Large crystals of moonstone in Rabb Canyon area, Grant County. Good crystals and several types of twins at several localities.

Periclase.—Crystals in periclase marble: South Canyon district.

Phosgenite.—Notable crystals found many years ago in Organ district.

Pickeringite.—Deposits in several counties.

Piedmontite.—Interesting occurrence: Glenwoody district.

Plagioclase.—Notable aggregates of cleavelandite: Petaca district.

Plattnerite.—Tiny crystals associated with murdochite: Hansonburg district.

Plumbojarosite.—*Type locality for this new species:* Cooks Peak district. Also conspicuous in Central district.

Polyhalite.—Carlsbad Potash district: second record for U. S. Abundant.

Pseudobrookite.—Taylor Creek district: third record for U. S.; six new prism forms.

Psilomelane.—Important ore mineral in several districts.

Pyrargyrite.—Formerly mined in several districts.

Pyrite.—Common and widespread. Many excellent crystals.

Pyrolusite.—Important ore mineral. Magnificent crystals at Lake Valley.

Pyromorphite.—Locally abundant in several districts.

Quartz.—Many forms of quartz were utilized extensively for centuries by prehistoric peoples for various kinds of artifacts. Doubly terminated crystals (Pecos diamonds) are extraordinarily abundant in Permian gypsum at certain places in several counties along Pecos River. Pseudocubic crystals: Chaves and Eddy Counties. Agatized wood locally abundant in several counties.

Ramsdellite.—One of three world localities furnishing *type material for this new species,* described in 1943: Lake Valley district.

Rhodonite.—Showy specimens: Kingston district.

Samarskite.—Excellent specimens: Petaca district. Age—300 million years.

Santafeite.—*New species being described:* Grants district.

Scheelite.—In several districts. A notable association with fluorite: El Porvenir district.

Sepiolite.—First discovery in U. S. Apparently Grant County has the largest deposit in U. S.

Serpentine.—*Type locality for the variety ricolite:* Ricolite district.

Sillimanite.—Sillimanite schist employed extensively by prehistoric Indians for axes.

Silver.—Numerous notable occurrences.

Skutterudite.—See Nickel-skutterudite.

Smithsonite.—Notable occurrence in Magdalena district of green smithsonite of gem quality (= herrerite = bonamite). Smithsonite has replaced such fossils as crinoid stems, crinoid calyces, and mollusk shells.

Soddyite.—First occurrence of this mineral found in sedimentary rocks: Laguna district.

Sphalerite.—Important ore mineral in many districts. Marmatite occurs in several districts.

Spinel.—Pleonaste at the north end of the Caballo Mountains was the subject of a master's thesis.

Spodumene.—Giant crystals, up to 14 ft long: Harding mine.

Spurrite.—Tres Hermanas district: first record for U. S. and third or fourth for the world.

Staurolite.—Twin crystals ("lucky stones," "fairy crosses") are especially abundant in Taos County.

Stromeyerite.—Reported to have been an important ore mineral in several mines.

Sulfur.—Notable occurrence of crystals currently forming in hot-spring deposits: Jemez Sulfur district.

Sylvite.—Carlsbad Potash district: third record for U. S. Chief ore mineral of the district.

Talc.—Mined during 1942–45 in the Hembrillo district. Also as bright blue material in Chloride Flat district.

Tantalite.—Shipments have been made from the Petaca and Harding Mine districts.

Tellurium.—Wilcox district and several other localities.

Tellurobismuthite.—Sylvanite district: *one of two type localities for this new species,* described in 1940.

Tennantite.—Hansonburg district.

Tetradymite.—At several localities.

Tetrahedrite.—Widespread and locally common.

Thorium mineral.—A new, still unnamed species described in 1928: Harding mine.

Torbernite.—Notable occurrences in White Signal and San Lorenzo districts.

Turquois.—New Mexico's best-known mineral. More turquois has been produced prehistorically and historically in this State than anywhere else in U. S.

Tyuyamunite.—Important ore mineral in the Todilto limestone ores of the Grants district. Also in several other districts.

Uraninite.—Widespread in several districts but generally not conspicuous.

Uranophane.—Showy rosettes in Grants district. Several other occurrences.

Vanadinite.—Excellent crystals, exhibiting new forms in several districts: Caballo Mountains, Hillsboro, and Lake Valley in Sierra County, and North Magdalena in Socorro County. Also, good specimens in several other districts.

Weissite.—Organ district.

Wheelerite.—*Type material for this new species,* described in 1874, came from northwestern New Mexico, probably Sandoval County.

Willemite.—Hillsboro district: excellent crystals. Socorro Peak district: new forms; the first crystals observed to exhibit tetartohedrism. Tres Hermanas district: unusual occurrence of excellent crystals; several carloads shipped as ore.

Wolframite.—Several notable occurrences of ferberite and huebnerite.

Wollastonite.—Several interesting occurrences.

Wulfenite.—Important ore mineral; excellent crystals in several districts. Notable hemimorphic forms in Orogrande district.

Xanthoconite.—Reported to have been mined at Cerrillos.

Yttrotantalite.—Found at four mines in the Petaca district.

Zoisite.—Showy specimens of thulite: Glenwoody district. Also in Iron Mountain No. 2 district.

REFERENCES

ABERT, J. W. (1848) *Report of Lieut. J. W. Abert, of his examination of New Mexico, in the years 1846–'47,* U. S. 30th Cong., 1st Sess., Senate Exec. Doc. 23, 130 p., 24 lithograph pls., map.

AITKENS, I. (1931) *Turquoise,* U. S. Bur. Mines Inf. Circ. 6491, 17 p.

——— (1932) *Quartz gem stones,* U. S. Bur. Mines Inf. Circ. 6561, 15 p.

ALLEN, KENNETH (1939) *Cow country bonanza,* New Mexico Mag., v. 17, no. 2, p. 20, 32, illus.

ANDERSON, E. C. (1946) *Annual report 1, for the fiscal year July 1, 1945—June 30, 1946,* New Mex. Bur. Mines and Min. Res. Ann. Rept., 1st, 42 p. Includes Bracewell, W. (1945), p. 26–42.

——— (1956) *Mining in the southern part of the Sangre de Cristo Mountains,* in *Guidebook of southeastern Sangre de Cristo Mountains, New Mexico,* New Mexico Geol. Soc. Seventh Field Conf., p. 139–142, map.

ANONYMOUS (1879) [Note on good specimens from the old Castilian turquois mine, Cerrillos], Eng. and Min. Jour., v. 29, p. 307.

——— (1880a) *Mining regions of New Mexico,* Min. World (Las Vegas), v. 1, no. 1, Sept., p. 1.

——— (1880b) *The Manzanos,* Min. World (Las Vegas), v. 1, no. 3, Nov., p. 4.

——— (1881a) [Note on Cerrillos turquois deposits] Eng. and Min. Jour., v. 31, p. 8–9.

——— (1881b) *The resources of New Mexico; Prepared under the auspices of the Bureau of Immigration, for the Territorial Fair to be held at Albuquerque, N. M., October 3d to 8th, 1881,* New Mexico Bur. Immigration, 64 [68] p., Santa Fe.

——— (1881c) *Silver Mountain mining district* (extracted from "The Prospector of the L. V. & St. L. M. & S. Co." [Las Vegas & St. Louis Mining & Smelting Co.]), Min. World (Las Vegas), v. 1, no. 5, Jan., p. 6.

——— (1881d) [News dispatch from Turquesa, Santa Fe County], Min. World (Las Vegas), v. 1, no. 5, Jan., p. 7.

——— (1881e) *Three days of observation spent in Los Cerrillos . . .,* Min. World (Las Vegas), v. 1, no. 6 [should be 9], May, p. 8.

——— (1882a) *Los Cerrillos,* Min. World (Las Vegas), v. 2, no. 19, July 15, p. 260–261.

——— (1882b) *The National Mining Exposition—New Mexico's magnificent exhibit. . . .,* Min. World (Las Vegas), v. 3, no. 2, Sept. 15, p. 22–23.

——— (1885) *Turquoise,* Min. World (Las Vegas), v. 5, no. 2, Oct., p. 23.

——— (1891a) [Note on occurrence of turquois near Paschal, said to be in Sierra County], Eng. and Min. Jour., v. 51, p. 751.

——— (1891b) *Turquoise in southwestern New Mexico,* Eng. and Min. Jour., v. 51, p. 719.

——— (1896) *The mines of New Mexico; Inexhaustible deposits of gold and silver,*

copper, lead, iron and coal; A mineral area unequalled in any State or Territory for the extent and value of its mines, New Mexico Bur. Immigration, 80 p., map, Santa Fe.
——— (1901a) *Mines and minerals of New Mexico; With some reference to the geological associations in the various camps of the Territory,* New Mexico Bur. Immigration, 136 p., Santa Fe.
——— (1901b) *Bernalillo County, New Mexico: The richest and most populous county in the Sunshine Territory; Its resources include agriculture, horticulture, sheep and wool, gold, coal and other minerals; manufactures, railroads, etc.,* New Mexico Bur. Immigration, 24 p., illus., Santa Fe.
——— (1902b) *Turquoise mining in Arizona and New Mexico,* Min. and Sci. Press, v. 85, p. 102–103.
——— (1906) *Bernalillo County: A description of the smallest and the richest county of New Mexico,* New Mexico Bur. Immigration, 45 p., illus., Santa Fe.
——— (1908a) *Burro Mountain turquoise,* South-Western Mines, v. 1, no. 1, Oct. 5, p. 1–2, 1 fig.
——— (1908c) *Mining activity in the Sandias,* South-Western Mines, v. 1, no. 1, Oct. 5, p. 5.
———(1908d) *New gold camp of Sylvanite,* South-Western Mines, v. 1, no. 2, Nov. 5, p. 1.
——— (1909a) *Black Mesa district,* South-Western Mines, v. 1, no. 4, Jan. 5, p. 5.
——— (1909b) *Gold in the Black Range, Socorro* [Sierra] *County, New Mexico,* South-Western Mines, v. 1, no. 4, Jan. 5, p. 5.
——— (1909c) *Gold in the Black Range, New Mexico,* South-Western Mines, v. 1, no. 9, June 5, p. 8.
——— (1909d) *Gold near Mountainair,* South-Western Mines, v. 1, no. 9, June 5, p. 8.
——— (1910d) *The mines of Colfax County, New Mexico,* South-Western Mines, v. 2, no. 8, Aug., p. 3–5, illus.
——— (1910e) *Tiffany turquoise mines robbed by Santa Domingo Indians,* South-Western Mines, v. 2, no. 8 [should be 9], Nov., p. 9.
——— (1946a) [News items concerning ricolite and bastnaesite], Min. Jour., v. 29, no. 17, p. 26.
——— (1941) *Age of the Cochise culture stages,* in Sayles, E. B., and Antevs, E., *The Cochise Culture,* Medallion Papers No. 29 (Gila Pueblo, Globe, Arizona), p. 31–56.
Antisell, Thomas (1856) *Geological report* [Parke's reconnaissance near the 32d parallel], in *Reports of explorations and surveys, to ascertain the most practicable and economical route for a railroad from the Mississippi River to the Pacific Ocean,* U. S. 33d Cong., 2d Sess., Senate Exec. Doc. 78, v. 7, pt. 2, 204 p., maps.
Ayer, E. E. (1916) *The Memorial of Fray Alonso de Benavides, 1630* (Translation by Mrs. E. E. Ayer), 309 p., Chicago.
Bailey, J. W. (1848) *Notes concerning the minerals and fossils, collected by Lieutenant J. W. Abert, while engaged in the geographical examination of New Mexico, by J. W. Bailey, professor of chemistry, mineralogy, and geology, at the United States Military Academy,* U. S. 30th Cong., 1st Sess., Senate Exec. Doc. 23, p. 131–132, illus.
Ball, S. H. (1913) *Sandstone copper deposits at Bent, New Mexico,* Min. and Sci. Press, v. 107, p. 132–135, 2 figs., map.
——— (1941) *The mining of gems and ornamental stones by American Indians,* Smithsonian Inst. Bur. Am. Ethnology Bull. 128, Anthropol. Papers 13, 77 p., illus. (incl. maps).
Bancroft, Hubert H. (1888) *History of the Pacific States of North America,* v. 12: *Arizona and New Mexico, 1530–1888,* 829 p., San Francisco.
Bandelier, A. F. (1890) *Final report of investigations among the Indians of the south-*

western United States, carried on mainly in the years from 1880 to 1885, Archaeol. Inst. America Papers, American Ser. 3, pt. 1, 323 p.

——— (1892) Part 2 of Bandelier (1890), ibid., American Ser. 4, pt. 2, 591 p.

BLAKE, W. P. (1856a) *Report on the geology of the route: No. 1, General report upon the geological collections* [Whipple's reconnaissance near the 35th parallel], in *Reports of explorations and surveys, to ascertain the most practicable and economical route for a railroad from the Mississippi River to the Pacific Ocean,* U. S. 33d Cong., 2d Sess., Senate Exec. Doc. 78 and House Exec. Doc. 91, v. 3, pt. 4, 119 p., illus. (incl. map).

——— (1856b) *Report on the geology of the route, near the thirty-second parallel: Prepared from the collection and notes of Capt. Pope,* in *Reports of explorations and surveys. . . .,* U. S. 33d Cong., 2d Sess., Senate Exec. Doc. 78, v. 2, 50 p., map.

——— (1858) *The chalchihuitl of the ancient Mexicans: Its locality and association, and its identity with turquoise,* Am. Jour. Sci. (2) v. 25, p. 227–232.

——— (1859a) *Observations on the mineral resources of the Rocky Mountain Chain, near Santa Fe, and the probable extent southwards of the Rocky Mountain gold field,* Boston Soc. Nat. Hist. Proc., v. 7, p. 64–70; Min. Mag., v. 1, p. 22–27.

——— (1859b) *Observations on the geology of the Rocky Mountain Chain in the vicinity of Santa Fe, New Mexico,* Edinburgh New Phil. Jour., n. s., v. 10, p. 301–304; Am. Assoc. Adv. Sci. Proc., v. 13, p. 314–319 (1860).

——— (1883) *New locality of the green turquois known as chalchuite, and on the identity of turquois with the callais or callaina of Pliny,* Am. Jour. Sci. (3) v. 25, p. 197–200.

——— (1899) *Aboriginal turquoise mining in Arizona and New Mexico,* Am. Antiquarian, v. 21, p. 278–284.

BLOOD, C. C. (1916) *Pinos Altos district, Grant County, New Mexico,* Min. and Eng. World, v. 45, p. 659-660, 3 figs.

BLOOM, L. B. (1936) *Bourke on the Southwest, VIII,* New Mexico Hist. Rev., v. 11, p. 77–122.

BOLTON, H. E. (1916) *Spanish exploration in the Southwest, 1542–1706,* 487 p., New York, Charles Scribner's Sons.

BRAND, D. D., HAWLEY, F. M., HIBBEN, F. C., and others (1937) *Tseh So, a small house ruin, Chaco Canyon, New Mexico (preliminary report),* Univ. New Mexico Bull. 308, Anthropol. ser., v. 2, no. 2, 174 p., illus.

BREVOORT, ELIAS (1874) *New Mexico: Her natural resources and attractions, being a collection of facts, mainly concerning her geography, climate, population, schools, mines and minerals, agricultural and pastoral capacities, prospective railroads, public lands, and Spanish and Mexican land grants,* 176 p., Santa Fe.

BRYAN, KIRK (1938) *Prehistoric quarries and implements of pre-Amerindian aspect in New Mexico,* Science, v. 87, p. 343–346.

——— (1939) *Stone cultures near Cerro Pedernal and their geological antiquity,* Texas Archeol. and Paleont. Soc. Bull., v. 11, p. 9–42, pls. 1–10 (incl. map).

——— (1941) *Correlation of the deposits of Sandia Cave, New Mexico, with the Glacial chronology,* in Hibben, F. C., *Evidences of early occupation in Sandia Cave, New Mexico, and other sites in the Sandia-Manzano region,* Smithsonian Misc. Coll., v. 99, no. 23, p. 45–64, illus. (incl. map).

CALVIN, ROSS (1951) *Lieutenant Emory reports: A reprint of Lieutenant W. H. Emory's Notes of a Military Reconnoissance; Introduction and notes by Ross Calvin,* 208 p., maps, Albuquerque, Univ. New Mexico Press.

CARNOT, A. (1895) *Sur la composition chimique des turquoises,* Société Française de Minéralogie Bull., v. 18, p. 119–123; (Abstract) Zeitschrift für Krystallographie und Mineralogie, Band 27, p. 615–616 (1896–97).

Chase, C. A., and Muir, Douglas (1923) *The Aztec mine, Baldy, New Mexico,* Am. Inst. Min. Met. Eng. Trans., v. 68, p. 270–281, map.

Church, F. S., and Hack, J. T. (1939) *An exhumed erosion surface in the Jemez Mountains, New Mexico,* Jour. Geology, v. 47, p. 613–629, 10 figs. (incl. maps).

Clarke, F. W. (1884) *A report of work done in the Washington Laboratory during the fiscal year 1883-84,* U. S. Geol. Survey Bull. 9, 40 p.

——— (1903) *Mineral analyses from the laboratories of the United States Geological Survey, 1880 to 1903,* U. S. Geol. Survey Bull. 220, 119 p.

——— (1915) *Analyses of rocks and minerals from the Laboratory of the United States Geological Survey, 1880 to 1914,* U. S. Geol. Survey Bull. 591, 376 p.

———, and Diller, J. S. (1886) *Turquoise from New Mexico,* Am. Jour. Sci. (3) v. 32, p. 211–217.

———, and Diller, J. S. (1887) *Turquoise from New Mexico,* U. S. Geol. Survey Bull. 42, p. 39–44.

Cowan, J. L. (1908) *Turquoise mines of New Mexico,* Mineral Collector, v. 15, p. 110–112.

Crane, H. R. (1955) *Antiquity of the Sandia culture: Carbon-14 measurements,* Science, v. 122, p. 689–690.

Dana, E. S. (1892) *The System of Mineralogy of James Dwight Dana, 1837–1868,* 6th ed., 1134 p., illus., New York, John Wiley & Sons.

——— (1899) *First appendix to the Sixth edition of Dana's System of Mineralogy,* 75 p., New York, John Wiley & Sons.

Dana, J. D. (1837) *A system of mineralogy: Including an extended treatise on crystallography: With an appendix, containing the application of mathematics to crystallographic investigation, and a mineralogical bibliography. With two hundred and fifty wood cuts, and four copper plates, containing one hundred and fifty additional figures. By James Dwight Dana, A.M., Assistant in the Department of Chemistry, Mineralogy, and Geology, in Yale College; Member of the Yale Nat. Hist. Soc.; of the Conn. Acad. Sci.; Corresponding member of Acad. Nat. Sci. of Philadelphia, and of the Lyceum of Nat. Hist. of New York. "Haec studia nobiscum peregrinantur, rusticantur."* New Haven: Published by Durrie & Peck and Herrick & Noyes. Hitchcock & Stafford. Printers. 1837. xiv + 452 p. + 120 p. (total 586 p.), illus. In 1844, Wiley and Putnam published the second edition. Currently, John Wiley & Sons is publishing the seventh edition.

Dinsmore, C. A. (1910) *Azure turquoise mine, New Mexico,* Min. World, v. 33, p. 660.

Dunham, K. C., (1935) *The geology of the Organ Mountains, with an account of the geology and mineral resources of Dona Ana County, New Mexico,* New Mexico Bur. Mines and Min. Res. Bull. 11, 272 p., 14 pls. (incl. maps), 21 figs. (incl. maps).

Emory, W. H. (1848) *Notes of a military reconnoissance from Fort Leavenworth, in Missouri, to San Diego, in California, including part of the Arkansas, Del Norte, and Gila Rivers,* U. S. 30th Cong., 1st Sess., Senate Exec. Doc. 7, p. 5–126; also as House Exec. Doc. 41. See Calvin, Ross (1951) for reprint edition.

Endlich, F. M. (1883) *The mining regions of southern New Mexico,* Am. Naturalist, v. 17, p. 149–157, pl. 3.

Entwistle, L. P. (1944a) *Manganiferous iron-ore deposits near Silver City, New Mexico,* New Mexico Bur. Mines and Min. Res. Bull. 19, 70 p., 10 pls. (incl. maps), 11 figs. (incl. maps).

Farrington, O. C. (1900) *New mineral occurrences; Caledonite,* Field Columbian Mus. Pub. 44, Geol. ser., v. 1, no. 7, p. 224–226, fig. 3.

——— (1903) *Gems and gem minerals,* 229 p., illus., Chicago, A. W. Mumford.

Fenderson, W. C. (1897) *Turquoise mining in New Mexico,* Min. and Sci. Press, v. 74, p. 192.

Foshag, W. F. (1920) *Illustration of the hexagonal system; Hematite from New Mexico,* Am. Mineralogist, v. 5, p. 149–150, 2 figs.

——— (1955) *Chalchihuitl—A study in jade,* Am. Mineralogist, v. 40, p. 1062–1070.

FRAZER, PERSIFOR, JR. (1869) *Mines and minerals of Colorado* [and New Mexico], U. S. Geol. and Geog. Surveys Terr. (Hayden) Prelim. Field Rept., p. 101–130; 3d Ann. Rept., p. 201–228 (1873).

FROST, MAX (1890) *New Mexico: Its resources, climate, geography, and geological condition,* New Mexico Bur. Immigration (Max Frost, Secretary and editor), 216 p., Santa Fe.

———, and WALTER, P. A. F. (1906) *Santa Fe County: The heart of New Mexico, rich in history and resources,* New Mexico Bur. Immigration, 145 p., illus., Santa Fe.

GENTH, F. A. (1854) *On a new meteorite from New Mexico,* Am. Jour. Sci. (2) v. 17, p. 239–240.

——— (1890) *Gold in turquois from Los Cerillos, New Mexico,* in *Contributions to mineralogy, No. 48,* Am. Jour. Sci. (3) v. 40, p. 115–116.

———, and RATH, GERHARD VOM (1885) *On the vanadates and iodyrite, from Lake Valley, Sierra Co., New Mexico,* Am. Phil. Soc. Proc., v. 22, p. 363–375, 4 figs. Also as: *Über Vanadate und Jodsilber von Lake Valley, Donna Anna County, New Mexico,* Zeitschrift für Krystallographie und Mineralogie, Band 10, p. 458–474, pl. 14, figs. 1–5.

GILLERMAN, ELLIOT [G.] (1952a) *Fluorspar deposits of Burro Mountains and vicinity, New Mexico,* U. S. Geol. Survey Bull. 973–F, p. 261–289, pls. 46–59 (incl. maps), fig. 30 (map).

———, and WHITEBREAD, D. H. (1956) *Uranium-bearing nickel-cobalt-native silver deposits, Black Hawk district, Grant County, New Mexico,* U. S. Geol. Survey Bull. 1009–K, p. 283–313, pls. 14–16 (incl. maps), figs. 44–48 (incl. maps).

GRATON, L. C. (1933) *Life and scientific work of Waldemar Lindgren,* in *Ore deposits of the Western States (Lindgren volume),* Am. Inst. Min. Met. Eng., p. xiii-xxii.

GREGG, JOSIAH (1844; 1933) *Commerce of the Prairies (The journal of a Santa Fe trader),* 438 p., Dallas, Texas, Southwest Press; 1st ed., 1844; reprint ed., 1933.

HADLEY, W. C. (1881) *Mora County mineral,* Min. World (Las Vegas), v. 1, no. 8, April, p. 4.

HALLENBECK, CLEVE (1940) *Álvar Núñez Cabeza de Vaca; The journey and route of the first European to cross the continent of North America, 1534–1536,* 326 p., maps, Glendale, California, A. H. Clark Co.

HAMMOND, G. P. (1927) *Don Juan de Oñate and the founding of New Mexico (A new investigation . . . from the Archivo General de Indias, Seville, Spain),* Hist. Soc. New Mexico Pub. in History, v. 2, 228 p.

———, and REY, AGAPITO (1927) *The Gallegos Relation of the Rodríguez expedition to New Mexico,* Hist. Soc. New Mexico Pub. in History, v. 4, 69 p.

———, and REY, AGAPITO (1929) *Expedition into New Mexico made by Antonio de Espejo, 1582–1583, as revealed in the journal of Diego Pérez de Luxán, a member of the party,* Quivira Soc. Pub., v. 1, 143 p., maps, Los Angeles, The Quivira Society.

———, and REY, AGAPITO (1940) *Narratives of the Coronado expedition, 1540–1542,* Coronado Cuarto Centennial Pub., 1540–1940, v. 2, 413 p., Univ. New Mexico Press.

HARLEY, G. T. (1934) *The geology and ore deposits of Sierra County, New Mexico,* New Mexico Bur. Mines and Min. Res. Bull. 10, 220 p., 11 pls. (incl. maps), 19 figs. (incl. maps).

HARRINGTON, E. R. (1939a) *Forests turned to stone,* New Mexico Mag., v. 17, no. 4, p. 16–17, 42, 8 figs.

——— (1939b) *Digging for turquoise in America's first mines,* New Mexico Mag., v. 17, no. 7, p. 12–13, 45–46, 7 figs. (incl. map).

——— (1939c) *Desert gold* [New Placers and Old Placers districts], New Mexico Mag., v. 17, no. 11, p. 10–11, 36–38, 7 figs. (incl. map).

——— (1940a) *Chalchihuitl—A story of early turquoise mining in the Southwest,* Eng. and Min. Jour., v. 141, no. 6, p. 57–58, 3 figs.

——— (1941) *Gold camp* [Cochiti district], New Mexico Mag., v. 19, no. 3, p. 14–15, 34, 4 figs. (incl. map).

——— (1944) *Ghost town silver,* Mines Mag., v. 34, p. 587–588, 594, 614, 7 figs.

Henderson, C. W. (1933) *The history and influence of mining in the western United States,* in *Ore deposits of the Western States (Lindgren volume),* Am. Inst. Min. Met. Eng., p. 730–784.

Henderson, E. P. (1934) *Two new meteoritic irons from New Mexico: The Grant meteorite and the Santa Fe meteorite,* Pop. Astron., v. 42, p. 511–515, 4 figs.

———, and Hess, F. L. (1933) *Corvusite and rilandite, new minerals from the Utah-Colorado carnotite region,* Am. Mineralogist, v. 18, p. 195–205, 2 figs.

Henrich, Carl (1887) *The San Pedro copper mine in New Mexico,* Eng. and Min. Jour., v. 43, p. 183.

Herrick, C. L. (1897) *The geology of a typical mining camp in New Mexico,* Am. Geologist, v. 19, p. 256–262.

——— (1900a) *Geological associations in New Mexico mining camps,* in Otero, M. A. (1900) p. 257–260.

Hess, F. L. (1912) *Vanadium in the Sierra de los Caballos, New Mexico,* Min. Science, v. 66, p. 216–217.

——— (1917b) *Nickel,* U. S. Geol. Survey Mineral Resources 1915, pt. 1, p. 743–766.

Hibben, F. C. (1941) *Evidences of early occupation in Sandia Cave, New Mexico, and other sites in the Sandia-Manzano region,* Smithsonian Misc. Coll., v. 99, no. 23, Pub. 3636, 44 p., illus. (incl. map).

Hidden, W. E. (1893) *Two new localities for turquoise,* Am. Jour. Sci. (3) v. 46, p. 400–402. Also as: *Zwei neue Fundorte Türkis,* Zeitschrift für Krystallographie und Mineralogie, Band 22, p. 552–553 (1893–94).

Hillebrand, W. F. (1889a) *Mineralogical notes,* Colorado Sci. Soc. Proc., v. 3, p. 38–47.

Howard, E. B. (1935) *Evidence of early man in North America,* Univ. Pennsylvania, Univ. Mus., Mus. Jour., v. 24, nos. 2–3, 158 p., illus.

Howe, C. S. (1881) *Mines and mining,* in Hazledine, W. C., *Report on Bernalillo County,* New Mexico Bur. Immigration, p. 7–10, Albuquerque.

Hyde, D. C. (not dated) *Mount Chalchuitl; Description of property and mines of the Turquoise Gold & Silver Mining Company, Los Cerrillos, Santa Fe County, New Mexico,* 15 p., 1 fig. (Promotional brochure published apparently between 1880 and 1890.)

Jicha, H. L., Jr. (1954a) *Paragenesis of the ores of the Palomas (Hermosa) district, southwestern New Mexico,* Econ. Geology, v. 49, p. 759–778, 11 figs. (incl. map); (Abstracts) Geol. Soc. America Bull., v. 64, p. 1442 (1953); New Mexico Geol. Soc. Program 8th Ann. Mtg., April 30–May 1, p. 5 (1954).

Johnson, D. W. (1903) *The geology of the Cerrillos Hills, New Mexico,* School of Mines (Columbia Univ.) Quart., v. 24, p. 173–246, illus., 303–350, 456–500 (1902); v. 25, p. 69–98, map (1903); Univ. New Mexico Bull. 28, Geol. ser., v. 2, pt. 2 (1903).

Jones, F. A. (1904) *New Mexico mines and minerals (World's Fair edition, 1904); Being an epitome of the early mining history and resources of New Mexican mines, in the various districts, down to the present time; Geology of the ore deposits, complete census of minerals, mineral and irrigation waters, table of altitudes and other general information,* 349 p., illus., Santa Fe.

——— (1905) *Gold and silver: New Mexico,* U. S. Geol. Survey Mineral Resources 1904, p. 200–203.

——— (1908a) *Epitome of the economic geology of New Mexico,* New Mexico Bur. Immigration, 47 p., Albuquerque.

——— (1908b) *Mineral wealth of New Mexico,* South-Western Mines, v. 1, no. 1, Oct. 5, p. 6.

——— (1908c) *New gold camp of Sylvanite, New Mexico,* South-Western Mines, v. 1, no. 3, Dec. 5, p. 1, 6, 4 figs. (incl. map).

——— (1908d) *Sylvanite, New Mexico, the new gold camp,* Eng. and Min. Jour., v. 86, p. 1101–1103, 5 figs. (incl. map).
——— (1909a) *History and mining of turquoise in the Southwest,* Min. World, v. 31, p. 1251–1252.
——— (1909d) *Notes on turquoise in the Southwest; Concerning its original workings, its geology and its modern method of mining,* South-Western Mines, v. 1, no. 12, Sept. 5, p. 1–2, 2 figs.
——— (1915) *The mineral resources of New Mexico,* New Mexico School of Mines, Min. Res. Survey Bull. 1, 77 p., map.

JUDD, N. M. (1925) *Everyday life in Pueblo Bonito,* Nat. Geog. Mag., v. 48, p. 227–262, illus.

JUNG, H. (1932) *Über Türkis,* Chemie der Erde, v. 7, p. 77–94. (Not seen; abstract by L. J. Spencer, 1934, Mineralog. Abs., v. 5, p. 279.)

KELLY, R. P. (1909) *The Red River district of New Mexico,* South-Western Mines, v. 1, no. 8, May 5, p. 1, 3.

KERNAL [Longuemare, Charles] (1880) *Socorro mining district; St. Felicite district,* Min. World (Las Vegas), v. 1, no. 3, Nov., p. 11.

KEYES, C. R. (1903a) *A remarkable silver pipe,* Eng. and Min. Jour., v. 76, p. 805.
——— (1903b) *Geology of the Apache Cañon placers,* Eng. and Min. Jour., v. 76, p. 966–967, 2 figs. (incl. map).
——— (1908) *Genesis of the Lake Valley, New Mexico, silver-deposits,* Am. Inst. Min. Eng. Bull. 19, p. 1–31, 8 figs. (incl. map); Trans., v. 39, p. 139–169 (1909).

KIDDER, A. V. (1932) *The artifacts of Pecos,* Peabody Foundation for Archaeology, Phillips Academy, Andover, Massachusetts, 314 p., illus.

KLUCKHOHN, CLYDE, and WYMAN, L. C. (1940) *An introduction to Navaho chant practice, with an account of the behaviors observed in four chants,* Am. Anthropological Assoc. Mem. 53 (Supp. to Am. Anthropologist, v. 42, no. 2, pt. 2), 204 p., 10 pls. (Minerals determined by George Switzer.)

KNAUS, C. L. (1948) *Sky stones,* New Mexico Mag., v. 26, no. 3, p. 22–23, 39–41, 7 figs.

KRIEGER, PHILIP (1932) *Geology of the zinc-lead deposit at Pecos, New Mexico,* Econ. Geology, v. 27, p. 344–364, 8 figs., p. 450–470, figs. 9–16.
——— (1935) *Primary native silver ores at Batopilas, Mexico, and Bullard's Peak, New Mexico,* Am. Mineralogist, v. 20, p. 715–723, 8 figs.

KUNZ, G. F. (1883) *American gems and precious stones,* in Williams, A., Jr., *Mineral resources of the United States* [1882], U. S. Geol. Survey, p. 483–499.
——— (1885) *Artificially stained turquoise from New Mexico,* Am. Assoc. Adv. Sci. Proc., v. 34, p. 240-241.
——— (1890) *Gems and precious stones of North America, a popular description of their occurrence, value, history, archaeology, and of the collections in which they exist . . .,* 336 p., illus., New York, Scientific Publishing Co.
——— (1893a) *Precious stones,* U. S. Geol. Survey Mineral Resources 1891, p. 539–551.
——— (1893b) *Precious stones,* U. S. Geol. Survey Mineral Resources 1892, p. 756–781.
——— (1904) *Turquoise; New Mexico,* U. S. Geol. Survey Mineral Resources 1903, p. 951–955. (This is a review of Johnson, D. W., 1903.)

LAKES, ARTHUR (1901) *The turquoise mines of the Cerillos Mountains in New Mexico,* Mines and Minerals, v. 21, p. 395–396.

LASKY, S. G. (1930) *Geology and ore deposits of the Ground Hog mine, Central district, Grant County, New Mexico,* New Mexico Bur. Mines and Min. Res. Circ. 2, 14 p., 1 pl.
——— (1935c) *Distribution of silver in base-metal ores,* Am. Inst. Min. Met. Eng. Trans., v. 115, p. 69–80.
——— (1947) *Geology and ore deposits of the Little Hatchet Mountains, Hidalgo and

Grant Counties, New Mexico, U. S. Geol. Survey Prof. Paper 208, 101 p., 27 pls. (incl. maps), 18 figs. (incl. maps).

———, and LOUGHLIN, G. F. (1943) *Minerals of the Magdalena district,* in Loughlin and Koschmann (1942) *Geology and ore deposits of the Magdalena mining district, New Mexico,* U. S. Geol. Survey Prof. Paper 200, p. 87–104, illus. [1943].

LEACH, A. A. (1916) *Black Hawk silver-cobalt ores,* Eng. and Min. Jour., v. 102, p. 456.

LECONTE, J. L. (1868) *Notes on the geology of the survey for the extension of the Union Pacific Railway, E. D., from the Smoky Hill River, Kansas, to the Rio Grande,* 76 p., map, Philadelphia.

LEE, W. T. (1913) *Graphite near Raton, New Mexico,* U. S. Geol. Survey Bull. 530, p. 371–374.

——— (1916) *The Aztec gold mine, Baldy, New Mexico,* U. S. Geol. Survey Bull. 620, p. 325–330, figs. 19–21 (incl. map).

LEESON, J. J. (1896) *Socorro County,* in Anonymous, *The mines of New Mexico. . . .,* New Mexico Bur. Immigration, p. 41–50.

LIBBY, W. F. (1952) *Radiocarbon dating,* 124 p., Chicago, Univ. Chicago Press.

——— (1954) *Chicago radiocarbon dates, IV,* Science, v. 119, p. 135–140.

LINDGREN, WALDEMAR (1908) *New occurrence of willemite and anhydrite* (Abstract), Science, v. 28, p. 933–934.

———, and BANCROFT, HOWLAND (1914) *Republic (Eureka) district* [Washington], U. S. Geol. Survey Bull. 550, p. 133–166.

———, GRATON, L. C., and GORDON, C. H. (1910) *The ore deposits of New Mexico,* U. S. Geol. Survey Prof. Paper 68, 361 p., 22 pls. (incl. maps), 33 figs. (incl. maps).

LOEW, OSCAR (1874) *On wheelerite, a new fossil resin,* Am. Jour. Sci. (3) v. 7, p. 571–572.

——— (1875a) *Report upon mineralogical, agricultural, and chemical conditions observed in portions of Colorado, New Mexico, and Arizona in 1873,* U. S. Geog. and Geol. Surveys West of the 100th Meridian (Wheeler), v. 3, pt. 6, p. 569–661.

——— (1875b) *Geological and mineralogical report on portions of Colorado and New Mexico, by Dr. O. Loew, mineralogist and chemist,* Rept. of Chief of Engineers, Appendix LL (Ann. Rept. of Lieut. G. M. Wheeler for fiscal year ending June 30, 1875): Appendix G-2 (U. S. 44th Cong., 1st Sess., House Exec. Doc. 1), pt. 2, v. 2, pt. 2, p. 1017–1036.

MACDONALD, BERNARD (1909) [Discussion of] *Genesis of the Lake Valley, New Mexico, silver-deposits,* Am. Inst. Min. Eng. Trans., v. 39, p. 850–856; Bull., v. 26, p. 211–216. (Discussion of Keyes, C. R., 1908.)

MANLY, R. L., JR. (1950) *The differential thermal analysis of certain phosphates,* Am. Mineralogist, v. 35, p. 108–115, 4 figs.

MARCOU, JULES (1856) *Report on the geology of the route: No. 2, Résumé and field notes, by Jules Marcou, geologist and mining engineer to the expedition; with a translation by William P. Blake* [Whipple's reconnaissance near the 35th parallel], in *Reports of explorations and surveys, to ascertain the most practicable and economical route for a railroad from the Mississippi River to the Pacific Ocean,* U. S. 33d Cong., 2d Sess., Senate Exec. Doc. 78 and House Exec. Doc. 91, v. 3, pt. 4, p. 121–164.

MARCY, R. B. (1850) *The report of Capt. R. B. Marcy's route from Fort Smith to Santa Fe,* U. S. 31st Cong., 1st Sess., Senate Exec. Doc. 64, p. 169–227.

MARTIN, G. A. (1908) *Sylvanite, New Mexico,* Eng. and Min. Jour., v. 86, p. 962–963.

MARTIN, P. S., RINALDO, J. B., and ANTEVS, ERNST (1949) *Cochise and Mogollon sites, Pine Lawn Valley, western New Mexico,* Fieldiana: Anthropology, v. 38, no. 1, 232 p., illus. (incl. maps).

———, RINALDO, J. B., and BLUHM, ELAINE (1954) *Caves of the Reserve area,* Fieldiana: Anthropology, v. 42, 227 p., illus.

MELINE, J. F. (1873) *Two thousand miles on horseback; A summer tour to the Plains, the Rocky Mountains, and New Mexico,* 4th ed., 317 p., New York, The Catholic Publication Soc.

MERRILL, G. P. (1895) *The onyx marbles; Their origin, composition, and uses, both ancient and modern,* Smithsonian Inst. Ann. Rept. 1893, Rept. U. S. Nat. Mus., p. 539–585, illus.

——— (1922) *Handbook and descriptive catalogue of the collections of gems and precious stones in the United States National Museum,* U. S. Nat. Mus. Bull. 118, 225 p., illus.

METZGER, O. H. (1938) *Gold mining in New Mexico,* U. S. Bur. Mines Inf. Circ. 6987, 71 p., 11 figs. (incl. maps).

NEWBERRY, J. S. (1861) *Geological report,* in Ives, J. C., *Report upon the Colorado River of the West, explored in 1857 and 1858 by Lieutenant Joseph C. Ives, Corps of Topographical Engineers, under the direction of the Office of Explorations and Surveys,* U. S. War Dept., U. S. 36th Cong., 1st Sess., House Exec. Doc. 90, pt. 3, 154 p,. illus. (incl. maps).

——— (1876) *Geological report,* in Macomb, Capt. J. N., *Report of the exploring expedition from Santa Fé, New Mexico, to the junction of the Grand and Green Rivers of the great Colorado of the West, in 1859,* U. S. Army Engineer Dept., p. 9–118, illus. (incl. map). (Report prepared in 1860 but not published until 1876.)

OTERO, M. A. (1897) *Report of the Governor of New Mexico* [to the Secretary of the Interior] *for the year ending June 30, 1897,* Washington, D. C., p. 361–522.

——— (1899) *Report of the Governor of New Mexico* [to the Secretary of the Interior] *for the year ending June 30, 1899,* 376 p., illus. (incl. maps), Washington, D. C.

——— (1900) *Report of the Governor of New Mexico* [to the Secretary of the Interior] *for the year ending June 30, 1900,* 445 p., Washington, D. C.

——— (1901) *Report of the Governor of New Mexico* [to the Secretary of the Interior] *for the year ending June 30, 1901,* 546 p., Washington, D. C.

——— (1902) *Report of the Governor of New Mexico to the Secretary of the Interior, 1902,* 638 p., Washington, D. C.

——— (1903) *Report of the Governor of New Mexico to the Secretary of the Interior, 1903,* 661 p., Washington, D. C.

OWEN, R. E., and COX, E. T. (1865) *Report on the mines of New Mexico,* 59 p., Washington, D. C. "Published by [Judge] John S. Watts; Gideon & Pearson, Printers." The first part of this report, p. 1–46, is by Prof. Richard E. Owen, Geologist (dated at Indiana State University, Bloomington, Indiana, January 1, 1865); the second part, p. 47–59, is by E. T. Cox, Geologist and Chemist (dated at New Harmony, Indiana, February 20, 1865).

PAIGE, SIDNEY (1909) *The Hanover iron-ore deposits, New Mexico,* U. S. Geol. Survey Bull. 380, p. 199–214, map.

——— (1912) *The Origin of turquoise in the Burro Mountains, New Mexico,* Econ. Geology, v. 7, p. 382–392.

PENFIELD, S. L. (1886) *Crystallized vanadinite from Arizona and New Mexico,* Am. Jour. Sci. (3) v. 32, p. 441–443, fig. 4.

——— (1900) *On the chemical composition of turquoise,* Am. Jour. Sci. (4) v. 10, p. 346–350; Zeitschrift für Krystallographie und Mineralogie, Band 33, p. 542–547; Yale Univ. Bicen. Pub. Contr. Mineralogy, p. 365–370 (1901).

PEPPER, G. H. (1905) *Ceremonial objects and ornaments from Pueblo Bonito, New Mexico,* Am. Anthropologist, n. s., v. 7, p. 183–197, pls. 17–20, figs. 3–5.

——— (1909) *The exploration of a burial-room in Pueblo Bonito, New Mexico,* in *Anthropological essays: Putnam Anniversary volume,* New York, G. E. Stechert & Co., p. 196–252, 7 pls., 7 figs.

PETERS, E. D. (1882) *Notes on the Oscura copper-fields, and other mines in New Mexico,* Eng. and Min. Jour., v. 34, p. 270–272.

PETERSEN, [CARL] THEODOR (1898) *Zur Kenntniss der natürlichen Phosphate; 1. Türkis aus Neu-Mexiko,* Jahresbericht des Physikalischen Vereins zu Frankfurt am Main (1896–1897), p. 77–80 (1898); Neues Jahrbuch für Min., Geol., und Pal. (1900), Band 2, Ref. p. 31.

PICKARD, B. O. (1912) *The Ore* [Oro] *Grande mine in Grant County, New Mexico,* Min. Science, v. 65, p. 166–168, 3 figs.

POGUE, J. E. (1915) *The turquois: A study of its history, mineralogy, geology, ethnology, archaeology, mythology, folklore, and technology,* Nat. Acad. Sci. Mem., v. 12, pt. 2, Mem. 3, 162 p., front. in color, 22 pls., 5 figs.

POUGH, F. H. (1941) *Occurrence of willemite,* Am. Mineralogist, v. 26, p. 92–102.

——— (1954) *A field guide to rocks and minerals,* 333 p., illus. (some in color), Boston, Houghton Mifflin Co.

RAMDOHR, PAUL (1948) *Klockmann's Lehrbuch der Mineralogie, neu herausgegeben von Paul Ramdohr,* 13th ed., 674 p., 606 figs., Stuttgart, Ferdinand Enke.

RAUNHEIM, S. E. (1891) *Santa Fe, N. Mex.,* Eng. and Min. Jour., v. 51, p. 654–655.

RAYMOND, R. W. (1869) *Mineral resources of the States and Territories west of the Rocky Mountains,* U. S. Treasury Dept., 256 p., Washington, D. C.

——— (1870) *Statistics of mines and mining in the States and Territories west of the Rocky Mountains,* 2d rept., U. S. Treasury Dept., 805 p., Washington, D. C.

REID, G. D. (1903) *The Burro Mountain turquoise district,* Eng. and Min. Jour., v. 75, p. 786.

REITER, PAUL (1938) *The Jemez Pueblo of Unshagi, New Mexico; With notes on the earlier excavations at "Amoxiumqua" and Giusewa,* Univ. New Mexico Bull. 326, Monograph ser., v. 1, no. 4, 92 p., illus.

ROBERTS, F. H. H., JR. (1929) *Shabik'eshchee Village: A late Basket Maker site in the Chaco Canyon, New Mexico,* Smithsonian Inst. Bur. Am. Ethnology Bull. 92, 164 p., illus.

ROBINSON, SAMUEL (1825) *A catalogue of American minerals, with their localities; Including all which are known to exist in the United States and British Provinces, and having the towns, counties, and districts in each state and province arranged alphabetically; With an appendix, containing additional localities and a tabular view,* 316 p., Boston, Cummings, Hilliard, & Co.

RÖSLER, H. (1902) [Title not known; Pogue, 1915, cites reference to origin of turquois at Cerrillos], Neues Jahrbuch für Min., Geol., und Pal., Beilage Band 15, p. 286. (Not seen.)

SCHOLES, F. V. (1935) *Civil government and society in New Mexico in the seventeenth century,* New Mexico Hist. Rev., v. 10, p. 71–111.

——— (1942) *Troublous times in New Mexico, 1659–1670,* Hist. Soc. New Mexico Pub. in History, v. 11, 276 p.

SCHRADER, F. C., STONE, R. W., and SANFORD, SAMUEL (1917) *Useful minerals of the United States,* U. S. Geol. Survey Bull. 624, 412 p. (New Mexico list: p. 209–220.)

SILLIMAN, BENJAMIN, JR. (1880a) *The turquoise of New Mexico,* Science, v. 1, p. 289.

——— (1880b) *Report on the newly discovered auriferous gravels of the Upper Rio Grande del Norte in the counties of Taos and Rio Arriba, New Mexico,* 34 p., Omaha, Nebraska. (Not seen.)

——— (1880c) *Turquoise of New Mexico,* Am. Assoc. Adv. Sci. Proc., v. 29, p. 431–435 [1881].

——— (1881) *Turquoise of New Mexico,* Am. Jour. Sci. (3) v. 22, p. 67–71; (Abstract), Zeitschrift für Krystallographie und Mineralogie, Band 6, p. 519 (1882); (Abstract), Neues Jahrbuch für Min., Geol., und Pal., Band 1 (1883), Ref. p. 27.

SIMPSON, J. H. (1850) *Journal of a military reconnaissance from Santa Fe, New Mexico, to the Navajo country, made with the troops under the command of Brevet Lieutenant Colonel John M. Washington, chief of the 9th military department, and governor of New Mexico, in 1849, by James H. Simpson, A. M., First Lieutenant, Corps of Topographical Engineers,* U. S. 31st Cong., 1st Sess., Senate Exec. Doc. 64, p. 56–168, illus.

SMITH, E. P., and DOMINIAN, LEON (1904) *Notes on a trip to White Oaks, New Mexico,* Eng. and Min. Jour., v. 77, p. 799–800, 4 figs. (incl. map).

SMITH, R. V. (1908) *Mining in New Mexico during 1907,* Eng. and Min. Jour., v. 85, p. 198.

SNOW, C. H. (1891) *Turquoise in southwestern New Mexico,* Am. Jour. Sci. (3) v. 41, p. 511-512; (Abstract), Zeitschrift für Krystallographie und Mineralogie, Band 22, p. 422 (1893–94).

STATZ, B. A. (1908) *Magdalena mining district,* South-Western Mines, v. 1, no. 2, Nov. 5, p. 1, 3, 1 fig.

——— (1909a) *Notes on the gold ores of the San Pedro Mountain district, New Mexico,* South-Western Mines, v. 1, no. 4, Jan. 5, p. 1, 6, 1 fig.

——— (1912a) *The New Placer mining district, New Mexico,* Min. Science, v. 66, p. 167.

STERRETT, D. B. (1908a) *Precious stones,* U. S. Geol. Survey Mineral Resources 1907, pt. 2, p. 795–842.

———(1909) *Gems and precious stones,* U. S. Geol. Survey Mineral Resources 1908, pt. 2, p. 846.

——— (1911) *Gems and precious stones,* U. S. Geol. Survey Mineral Resources 1909, pt. 2, p. 789–795.

——— (1912) *Gems and precious stones,* U. S. Geol. Survey Mineral Resources 1911, pt. 2, p. 1066–1071.

——— (1913b) *Gems and precious stones,* U. S. Geol. Survey Mineral Resources 1912, pt. 2, p. 1055–1056.

——— (1916) *Gems and precious stones,* U. S. Geol. Survey Mineral Resources 1914, pt. 2, p. 334.

STEVENSON, J. J. (1881) *Report upon geological examinations in southern Colorado and northern New Mexico during the years 1878 and 1879,* U. S. Geog. and Geol. Surveys West of the 100th Meridian (Wheeler), v. 3–Supplement, 420 p., illus. (incl. maps).

TALMAGE, S. B., and WOOTTON, T. P. (1937) *The non-metallic mineral resources of New Mexico and their economic features (exclusive of fuels),* New Mexico Bur. Mines and Min. Res. Bull. 12, 159 p., 2 pls. (incl. map), 4 figs. (incl. maps).

TARR, TOM (1938) *Two mineral localities in New Mexico,* Rocks and Minerals, v. 13, p. 275–276.

TAYLOR, J. W. (1867) *Report of James W. Taylor, special commissioner for the collection of statistics upon gold and silver mining east of the Rocky mountains,* in Browne, J. R., and Taylor, J. W., *Reports upon the mineral resources of the United States,* U. S. Treasury Dept., p. 323–357. See p. 324–326 for New Mexico.

THORNTON, W. L. [should be "T."] (1893) *Report of the Governor of New Mexico to the Secretary of the Interior, 1893,* 33 p., Washington, D. C.

TWITCHELL, R. E. (1914) *The Spanish archives of New Mexico;* v. 1, 525 p.; v. 2, 683 p., Cedar Rapids, Iowa, The Torch Press.

VETANCURT, AGUSTÍN DE (1871) *Teatro mexicano; v. 3: Crónica de la provincia del Santo Evangelio de México,* 2d ed. (first published in 1697), México.

WELLS, E. H. (1918) *Manganese in New Mexico,* New Mexico School of Mines, Min. Res. Survey Bull. 2, 85 p., map.

———, and WOOTTON, T. P. (1932) *Gold mining and gold deposits in New Mexico,* New Mexico Bur. Mines and Min. Res. Circ. 5, 25 p. (For revised edition, see Wootton, 1940.)

WHIPPLE, A. W. (1856) [Report of Lieut. Whipple upon the route near the 35th parallel, explored in 1853 and 1854], in *Reports of explorations and surveys, to ascertain the most practicable and economical route for a railroad from the Mississippi River to the Pacific Ocean,* U. S. 33d Cong., 2d Sess., Senate Exec. Doc. 78, v. 3, 4 parts (separately paged).

WISLIZENUS, [F.] A. (1848) *Memoir of a tour to northern Mexico, connected with Col. Doniphan's expedition, in 1846 and 1847,* U. S. 30th Cong., 1st Sess., Senate Misc. Doc. 26, 141 p., maps.

WOOTTON, T. P. (1930) *Geologic literature of New Mexico,* New Mexico Bur. Mines and Min. Res. Bull. 5, 127 p.

——— (1940) *Gold mining and gold deposits in New Mexico (by E. H. Wells and T. P. Wootton, 1932),* rev. ed., New Mexico Bur. Mines and Min. Res. Circ. 5, 24 p.

WUESTNER, HERMAN (1930) *A check list of minerals from Kelly, New Mexico,* Rocks and Minerals, v. 5, p. 127–131, illus.

——— (1932) *The minerals of Silver City, New Mexico, district,* Rocks and Minerals, v. 7, p. 121–125.

ZALINSKI, E. R. (1907) *Turquoise in the Burro Mountains, New Mexico,* Econ. Geology, v. 2, p. 464–492, figs. 50–54; (Abstract), Zeitschrift für Krystallographie und Mineralogie, Band 46, p. 388–389 (1909).

——— (1908) *Turquoise mining, Burro Mountains, New Mexico,* Eng. and Min. Jour., v. 86, p. 843–846.